Pontcysyllte
Aqueduct and Canal
World Heritage Site

Pontcysyllte
Aqueduct and Canal
World Heritage Site

Peter Wakelin

United Nations
Educational, Scientific and
Cultural Organization

Pontcysyllte Aqueduct and Canal
inscribed on the World
Heritage List in 2009

ISBN 978-1-78461-146-0

First impression: 2015

British Library Cataloguing in Publication Data. A catalogue record for this book is available from the British Library.

First published in 2015 by the Canal & River Trust in partnership with the Royal Commission on the Ancient and Historical Monuments of Wales.

Printed by Y Lolfa, Talybont
Layout: stiwdio@ceri-talybont.com

Canal & River Trust
First Floor North, Station House, 500 Elder Gate, Milton Keynes MK9 1BB
T: 0303 040 4040
E: customer.services@canalrivertrust.org.uk
www.canalrivertrust.org.uk

Comisiwn Brenhinol Henebion Cymru
Royal Commission on the Ancient and Historical Monuments of Wales
Plas Crug, Aberystwyth, SY23 1NJ
T: 01970 621200
E: chc.cymru@cbhc.gov.uk / nmr.wales@rcahmw.gov.uk
www.cbhc.gov.uk / www.rcahmw.gov.uk

Publication has been with the generous support of:

UNESCO Cymru-Wales

Contents

How to use this guide

This book is an introduction and guide for visitors to Pontcysyllte Aqueduct and Canal World Heritage site and related places to visit nearby.

The introductory sections together with box features throughout tell the story of the canal and explain why it is of world significance. The site guide and detailed maps (pages 71–137), arranged from east to west, are designed to help you find places to visit or, if you prefer, to follow the canal on foot or by boat. A map on pages 72–3 shows the site as a whole. Further reading is suggested on page 142.

The canal's towpath is open to the public. Other rights of access are indicated in the guide. Please take care not to trespass on private land.

Much of the canal's towpath is suitable for wheelchairs and pushchairs, particularly the section from Trevor to Llangollen.

During your visit be considerate towards others so that you and they can appreciate this special place. The canal and its towpath are working heritage. In places the towpath is narrow and the gap between the railings of the Pontcysyllte aqueduct is wider than you might expect. Look after your children, don't try to cycle across the aqueducts or through the tunnel and take the opportunity for contemplation.

Information about staying in the area, special events and travelling around the World Heritage site can be found online at **www.pontcysyllte-aqueduct.co.uk**.

Please take care for your safety when visiting these areas and supervise children closely. Be aware of hazards, for example deep water, sudden drops, low headroom, road traffic and exposure.

Introduction:
The first industrial nation

Chirk tunnel. The engineers cut through the landscape to make a direct route

For over 200 years, Pontcysyllte aqueduct has amazed onlookers by carrying canal boats high in the air above their heads. This majestic masterpiece of engineering is one of the icons of the Industrial Revolution. In 2009 it was inscribed as a World Heritage site along with 11 miles of its canal and associated structures.

The canal was built between 1793 and 1808 to provide an efficient network of transport for industrial resources like coal, iron, limestone and slate. Many investors came together in the project. Landowners and industrialists needed better transport to exploit the mineral wealth of the area, while others were attracted by the opportunity to make a profit from the tolls the canal company would take on traffic. Thanks to the industrial development of the Denbighshire coalfield and others during the next half century, Wales became in 1851 the first nation in the world where more people worked in industry than agriculture.

The canal was designed by two of the outstanding figures in the history of civil engineering, William Jessop and Thomas Telford, who used new techniques to cut boldly through rugged terrain and cross two valleys. Their great aqueducts, tunnels, cuttings and embankments marked a significant stage in the evolution of transport, which previously had followed the lie of the land but now could command and shape the landscape. Jessop and Telford worked with a team of talented designers and craftsmen as well as hundreds of 'navvies' who dug the waterway.

The canal went on to carry industrial goods and materials for over a century. It

Left: Pontcysyllte aqueduct strides across the Dee valley with, beyond it, Cefn railway viaduct, from the next phase of industrialisation

The beautiful setting for the canal in the Vale of Llangollen is a buffer zone for the World Heritage site

helped transform the area into an industrial powerhouse. Today, this is one of the most popular waterways in Britain, a magnet for boaters, walkers and visitors who want to see some of the most remarkable achievements of the Industrial Revolution.

The inscription of Pontcysyllte Aqueduct and Canal on the World Heritage List means that its special significance must be conserved, protected and conveyed for future generations. A partnership of local councils, community groups, national organisations and charities works to ensure its future. A 'buffer zone' protects the setting of the canal and many associated features of interest.

Pronouncing 'Pontcysyllte' and names for the canal

Pontcysyllte means '**the bridge that joins**'. It is pronounced '**pont-cuss-ull-teh**'. (The Welsh '**ll**' is pronounced by putting your tongue to the roof of your mouth and blowing out at the sides.)

The World Heritage site is called **Pontcysyllte Aqueduct and Canal**. Its official name in Welsh is **Dyfrbont a Chamlas Pontcysyllte**.

Confusingly, the canal has been known by many different names. It was built as the **Ellesmere Canal** and its **Llangollen branch**. As a result of company mergers it became the **Ellesmere and Chester Canal** and then part of the **Shropshire Union Canal**. The canals were nationalised in 1948 and under British Waterways the route all the way from Hurleston Junction to Llangollen was known as the **Welsh Branch of the Shropshire Union Canal** and then the **Llangollen Canal**. Under the ownership today of the Canal & River Trust it is still called the Llangollen Canal.

Pontcysyllte aqueduct, the 'stream in the sky'

11

World Heritage site status

UNESCO (the United Nations Educational, Scientific and Cultural Organisation) maintains a list of sites under the World Heritage convention that are agreed to have outstanding universal cultural or natural value as part of the common heritage of humanity. Some of the most famous natural and cultural places in the world are World Heritage sites, including the **Grand Canyon**, the **Pyramids** and the **Great Wall of China**, and in Britain the **Giant's Causeway**, **Stonehenge**, the **Tower of London** and the cities of **Bath** and **Edinburgh**.

Some World Heritage sites are, like Pontcysyllte, testaments to outstanding engineering. The ancient Roman water-supply aqueduct of **Pont du Gard** in France became a World Heritage site in 1985. The **Canal du Midi** in France is an engineering masterpiece from the seventeenth century. The **Rideau Canal** in Canada is the best preserved waterway built in North America in the nineteenth century. Great feats of railway engineering on the list include the **Semmering Railway** in Austria and the **Darjeeling Himalayan Railway** in India.

Many World Heritage sites that bear witness to the Industrial Revolution are in Britain, such as the early cotton factories of **New Lanark** in Scotland and the **Derwent Valley** in Derbyshire, the metal-mining sites of **Cornwall and West Devon** and the ironworks and coal mines that can be visited at **Blaenavon** and **Ironbridge**.

Pontcysyllte Aqueduct and Canal was inscribed in 2009. The official inscription set out the grounds for its outstanding universal value:

That: The Pontcysyllte Aqueduct is a highly innovative monumental civil engineering structure, made using metal arches supported by high, slender masonry piers. It is the first great masterpiece of the civil engineer Thomas Telford and formed the basis of his outstanding international reputation. It bears witness to the production capacities of the British iron-making industry, which were unique at that time.

That: The intensive construction of canals in Great Britain, from the second half of the eighteenth century onwards, and that of the Pontcysyllte Canal in particular in a difficult region, bear witness to considerable technical interchanges and decisive progress in the design and construction of artificial waterways.

That: The Pontcysyllte Canal and its civil engineering structures bear witness to a crucial stage in the development of heavy cargo transport in order to further the Industrial Revolution. They are outstanding representatives of its new technical and monumental possibilities.

The Canal du Midi in France

The Castles and Town Walls of King Edward I in Gwynedd – four sites that show the power of medieval conquerors and masons, at Caernarfon, Conwy, Harlech and Beaumaris.

Ironbridge Gorge – often called the 'birthplace of industry', centred on the magnificent Iron Bridge of 1779, which demonstrated the potential of cast-iron construction. Award-winning museums tell the story of early industrialisation.

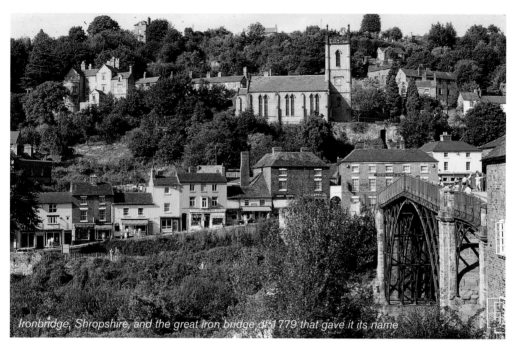

Ironbridge, Shropshire, and the great iron bridge of 1779 that gave it its name

Liverpool Maritime and Mercantile City – a city and docklands that bear witness to the development of a world-wide trading centre with modern dock technology, transport systems and port management.

Blaenavon Industrial Landscape – an upland landscape of iron making and coal mining in south Wales that shows the impact of early industrialisation on technology, transport, industry and society.

Consideration is being given to nominating the **slate industry of north Wales**, focused on sites such as the Ffestiniog Railway and the National Slate Museum at Llanberis.

Blaenavon ironworks is the best preserved of its type and period in the world

Canals and engineering in the Industrial Revolution

The Industrial Revolution was one of the most remarkable periods of change in history. It transformed technology, work and living conditions. Its consequences were far-reaching and they continue even today. The sudden growth of industries began in late eighteenth-century Britain, then spread to Europe, North America and onwards to other parts of the world.

Some of the most important characteristics of the Industrial Revolution are illustrated by Pontcysyllte Aqueduct and Canal. The engineering to build the canal represents the improvement of transport, the application of new technologies, the growth of capital investment and the expansion of trade between different regions. Rapid increases in population and industrial output during the Industrial Revolution are illustrated even today in communities like Llangollen, Cefn Mawr and Ruabon and by the remains of industries all along the canal. Canals were built above all to carry coal, which was the raw material that began the shift from renewable energy to fossil fuels. This change enabled the economy to grow faster than ever before, but it had environmental consequences from which the world still suffers.

The great French historian Fernand Braudel wrote about the conditions that made for extraordinary economic growth in Britain: 'perhaps most of all, there was the proliferation of new means of transport, something which preceded the demands of trade, and then helped it expand'. Inland waterways were the arteries of the Industrial Revolution in Britain, at a time when roads and railways were rudimentary. They represented a new phase in the history of inland navigation − the first nation-wide network of waterways for efficient industrial transport. But canals were much older inventions. The world's first transport canal was in China in about 300BC, and artificial waterways were common in the Roman Empire. Others were built in the Middle Ages in Italy, France and Saxony. The first long-distance canal in Europe was the Canal du Midi, a 150-mile link between the Atlantic and Mediterranean coasts of France completed in 1681.

In Britain, the coast and larger rivers had always been used by ships and boats to

An engraving of canal boats at Paddington bringing supplies into London

Left: P. J. de Loutherbourg's night-time depiction of the iron furnaces of Coalbrookdale in Shropshire in 1801 evokes the dynamic change brought about by the Industrial Revolution

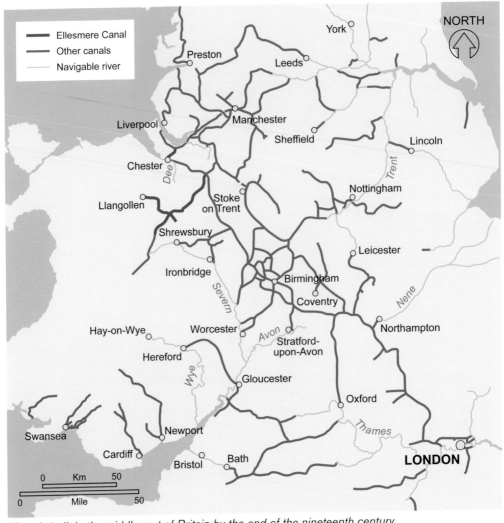

NORTH

York

Preston

Leeds

Liverpool

Manchester

Sheffield

Lincoln

Chester

Dee

Trent

Llangollen

Stoke on Trent

Nottingham

Shrewsbury

Leicester

Ironbridge

Severn

Birmingham

Coventry

Nene

Hay-on-Wye

Worcester

Avon

Stratford-upon-Avon

Northampton

Hereford

Wye

Gloucester

Oxford

Swansea

Newport

Thames

Cardiff

Bath

Bristol

LONDON

0   Km   50

0   Mile   50

Canals built in the middle part of Britain by the end of the nineteenth century

carry goods but landlocked areas also had potential for industrial development. In 1761, the Duke of Bridgewater completed a pioneering canal to connect his coal mines at Worsley in Lancashire to the river Mersey and Manchester. Its success inspired the evolution of a nation-wide network of canals between the 1760s and the 1830s which joined together sources of raw materials, processing sites and markets. In just twenty years between 1790 and 1810, more than 1,180 miles of inland waterways were built. The first canal in Wales was built by Thomas Kymer in 1766 to connect his coal mines in Carmarthenshire to a dock three miles away

at Kidwelly. Then, in the 1790s, a series of short and isolated but vitally important canals were built up the main valleys of south Wales to link ironworks and coal mines to the sea at Swansea, Neath, Cardiff and Newport.

Water carriage suited the transport of bulky and heavy materials that were essential to industrial growth. These included the millions of tons of coal that fuelled industries of all kinds and the many industrial and agricultural products that enabled urban expansion and population growth, including iron, stone, grain and textiles.

The Pontcysyllte project began in the 1790s, when industrialists and

A boat loaded with limestone is drawn eastwards along the canal past the dock and smoking limekilns at Froncysyllte, with Pontcysyllte aqueduct in the distance, 1830

entrepreneurs invested feverishly during what became known as the 'canal mania' and made possible an unprecedented scale of canal-building across the country. Acts of Parliament enabled the companies to buy land compulsorily and charge tolls for the goods they carried. The projects were devised by promoters, developed by innovative designers and built by tens of thousands of craftsmen and labourers (the navigators or 'navvies', page 30) who worked by hand with saws, axes, picks and shovels.

By the end of the nineteenth century, England and Wales were served by 5,340 miles of navigable canals and rivers – a vast system of industrial transport. These waterways were a huge achievement in their own right, but more importantly they dramatically enhanced the efficiency of the whole economy – by providing cheap fuel for industry, stimulating trade and fulfilling the needs of growing centres of population.

Looking up beneath Chirk aqueduct with the railway viaduct beyond

A history of Pontcysyllte Aqueduct and Canal

From idea to reality: the evolution of the project

All new canals in the Industrial Revolution began with people who had an idea and the will to push it forward. Such people could see opportunities to provide better transport to and from their own areas. They became a canal's 'promoters'.

The project that was to produce Pontcysyllte Aqueduct and Canal began in 1789, when several people with industrial interests around Ruabon began to discuss how they might take the products of the Denbighshire coalfield cheaply to wider markets. The area was rich in coal, iron ore and clay, and reserves of limestone and slate also lay nearby, but it was shackled without cheap transport to the seaports, towns and other industrial regions. The idea of building a canal attracted enthusiastic support from businessmen, industrialists and entrepreneurs who wanted to sell their goods and materials, and from landowners over a wider area who wanted cheap access to coal and limestone to improve their land and saw opportunities to improve the value of their estates.

Initially, the promoters wanted to join the river Mersey to the rivers Dee and Severn. Doing so would forge the missing link in a chain of inland waterways between the ports of Liverpool and Bristol and connect the coalfield to the outside world in two different directions. Its objectives were stated as 'to pass near to or to communicate with several extensive Coal, Lime and Slate Works in the parishes of Chirk, Rhuabon and Llangollen … and with a branch to extend to Llanymynech', where there were further great limestone quarries. On 31 August 1791, this grand plan was approved at a public meeting at the Royal Oak inn in Ellesmere, a market town in Shropshire from which the new canal company took its name.

The exact route was still to be decided. No detailed maps had yet been made of Britain that showed the lie of the land and the relative heights of hills and valleys, let alone the underlying geology that would so much effect how a canal could be built. So the next step, as in building any canal of the time, was to commission surveyors to go out and inspect the possible routes and measure levels. Two local engineers who had expressed interests in the project, John Duncombe and William Turner, were asked to make recommendations. Soon afterwards the respected engineer William Jessop – described as 'an Engineer of approved Character and Experience' – was brought in to work with Duncombe and Turner and give an independent view.

In August 1792, Jessop recommended a route from the Mersey that would cut through the Wirral peninsula to Chester, then head south to Wrexham and Ruabon and continue to the Severn at Shrewsbury. The project was boldly ambitious: the canal would climb over 300 feet (91m) in height, and it would require the engineers to dig a tunnel near Ruabon longer than any yet seen and to build an aqueduct of unprecedented height across the Dee near the old bridge of Pont Cysyllte.

The promoters now needed investors to help them turn the project into reality. On 10 September 1792, shares in the new Ellesmere Canal Company were put on offer. It was the brief time of the 'canal mania' when tens of thousands of investors dashed to put their savings into canal schemes in the hope of making fortunes. People travelled from many parts of Britain,

Left: The Severn was a naturally navigable river at Shrewsbury but floods and droughts made it an unreliable transport route. Painting of the Welsh Bridge and trade at Frankwell quay by Paul Sandby

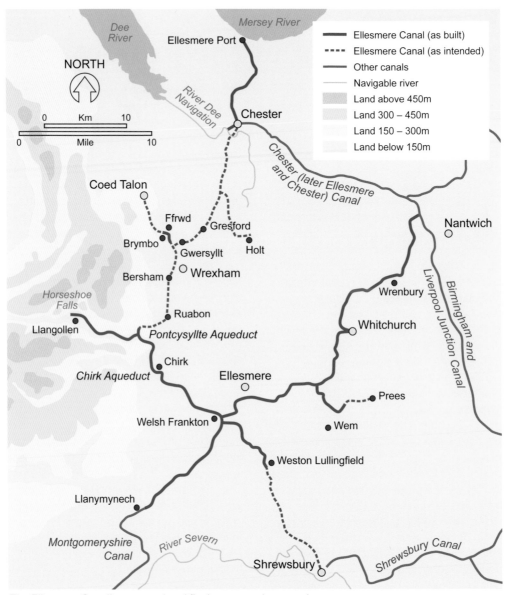

The Ellesmere Canal's proposed and final routes and connections

especially the midlands, for the chance to buy shares. A local newspaper, *The Chester Courant,* described dramatic scenes, and reported that 1,234 speculators had offered almost £1 million between noon and sunset:

> *Shrewsbury, about 16 miles from Ellesmere, was so crowded on the nights before and after the meeting that many people found very great difficulty getting accommodated:*

> *several gentlemen being obliged to take care of their own horses, cook their own victuals, and sleep two or three in a bed.*

The company scaled down what each of the 1,234 investors had offered and took in £246,500. In April 1793 an Act of Parliament was passed that authorised the company to raise the £400,000 that it was then estimated would be spent and another

A 1797 caricature of promoters during the Canal Mania

£100,000 if necessary. The Act also created legal powers to buy land at a fair price from landowners along the route, even if they did not wish to sell.

Some disagreements remained about the best route, but building started with the sections that would most quickly attract traffic and provide income from tolls. The first 9 miles were opened early in 1796, connecting the town of Chester across the Wirral to a wharf on the river Mersey – at a place that was to become 'Ellesmere Port'. This short section of canal carried coal from Lancashire and imports from Liverpool and was well used by passenger boats. Three more sections were begun in 1794 around Welsh Frankton near Ellesmere to serve the limestone quarries at Llanymynech and coal mines near Chirk.

The original idea for the canal continued to be rethought. The company gave up its goal of linking the Severn and the Mersey as the Severn was a notoriously unreliable river for navigation and coastal shipping already linked Liverpool and Bristol by sea. It realised that the focus should be on how best to take the minerals of the Denbighshire coalfield to surrounding markets and the Mersey. Two potential solutions remained: the original direct line north-eastwards from the coalfield to Chester, or going east and then north to meet the existing Chester Canal near Nantwich. The continuing uncertainty must have been frustrating for the engineers trying to progress with the project.

In 1800 William Jessop advised that it was 'wholly inadvisable to execute a canal between Pontcysyllte and Chester'. It would have been expensive and risky building the canal through the yet higher ground of the coalfield and it was becoming clearer that the mines and works spread through the area could be served by horse-worked railways from the canal head to wherever they were needed. As a result, the company decided once and for all to take the route through Shropshire to join the Chester Canal.

The main line from end to end – from the Chester Canal to the north side of Pontcysyllte aqueduct at Trevor – was completed in 1805. Work had begun a year earlier on a branch to bring water from the river Dee, which was now needed as the canal would no longer reach the planned water supplies from the river Clywedog west of Wrexham. The branch also served the town of Llangollen and was completed in 1808.

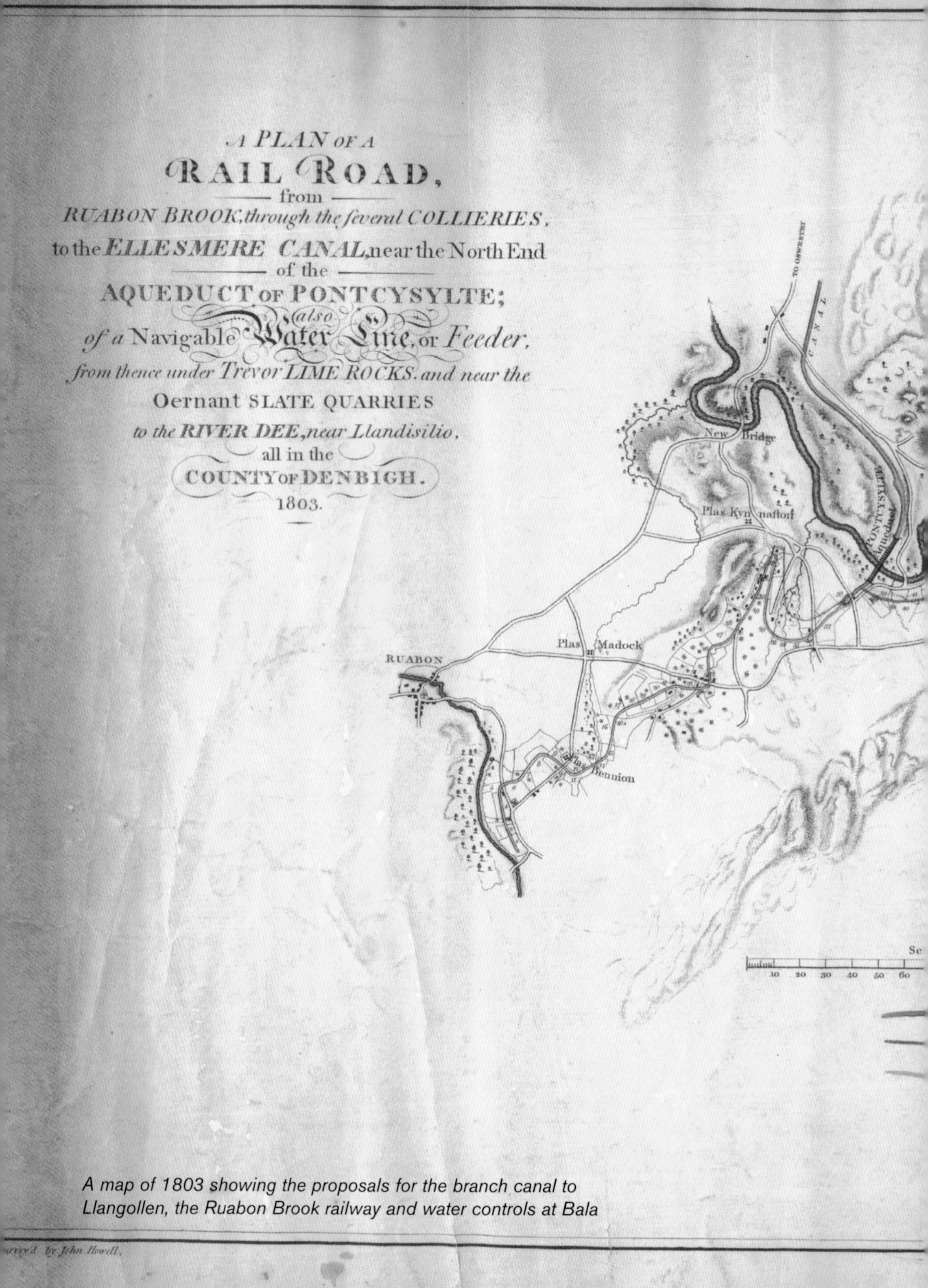
A PLAN OF A
RAIL ROAD,
from
RUABON BROOK, through the several COLLIERIES,
to the ELLESMERE CANAL, near the North End
of the
AQUEDUCT OF PONTCYSYLTE;
also
of a Navigable Water Line, or Feeder,
from thence under Trevor LIME ROCKS. and near the
Oernant SLATE QUARRIES
to the RIVER DEE, near Llandisilio,
all in the
COUNTY OF DENBIGH.
1803.
TO OSWESTRY
CANAL
New Bridge
Plas Kynnaston
PONTCYSYLTE Aqueduct
Plas Madock
RUABON
Plas Bennion
10 20 30 40 50 60
Survey'd by John Howell.

A map of 1803 showing the proposals for the branch canal to Llangollen, the Ruabon Brook railway and water controls at Bala

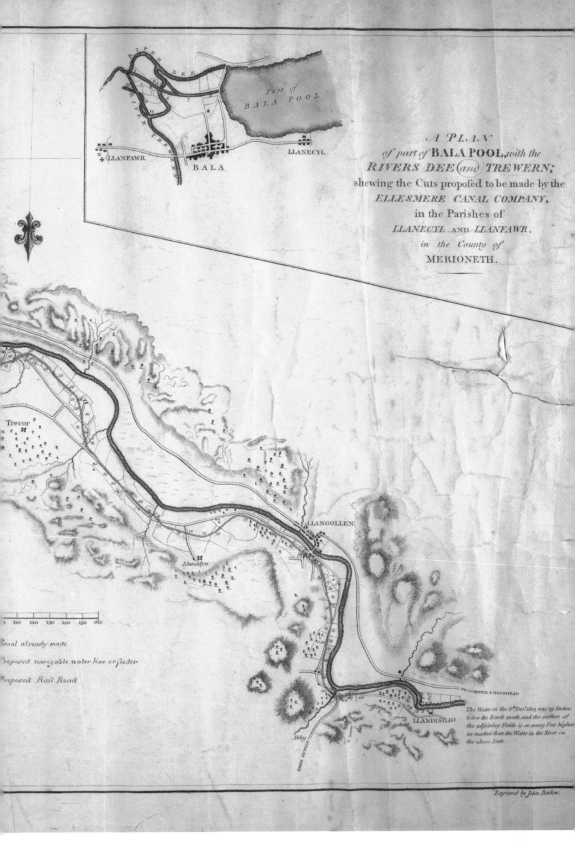

A PLAN
of part of BALA POOL, with the
RIVERS DEE (and) TREWERN;
shewing the Cuts proposed to be made by the
ELLESMERE CANAL COMPANY,
in the Parishes of
LLANECYL AND LLANFAWR,
in the County of
MERIONETH.

The Water on the 6th Decr 1805 was 19 Inches
below the Bench mark, and the surface of
the adjoining Fields is so many Feet higher
as marked than the Water in the River on
the above Date.

Canal already made
Proposed navigable water line or feeder
Proposed Rail Road

Engraved by John Barlow.

The industrial transport network the canal provided was added to by horse-worked tramroads (page 46). The most important tramroad linked to the Ellesmere Canal was the Ruabon Brook railway, which had probably been laid in the 1790s to bring materials to the aqueduct construction yard but was gradually extended as far north as Rhosllanerchrugog, four miles away. Others went to the Froncysyllte limestone quarries, the limestone outcrops west of Trevor, collieries near Chirk and slate quarries in the Horseshoe Pass and the Glyn valley. Around 1820 a short private canal was built by the industrialist Exuperius Pickering junior from the head of the main line at Trevor basin to his limekilns. It was extended at the end of the 1820s by Thomas Ward to serve his coal mines and the Plas Kynaston iron foundry, and a pottery and other industries sprang up beside it.

By the time the canal through the World Heritage site was finished, Britain was seen internationally as a leader in canal construction, visited by engineers from all over Europe and America. A decade after the opening of the canal, the French engineer Charles Dupin watched boats crossing Pontcysyllte aqueduct laden with coal and iron. He found the canal not only breathtaking in design but exemplary in purpose: a regional transport system that linked sources of minerals and products and connected to a wider network that gave access to Liverpool, Manchester, Ireland and London.

The national network continued to develop. The Montgomeryshire Canal was completed from the Ellesmere Canal's Llanymynech branch to Newtown by 1819. After the Ellesmere Canal Company and the Chester Canal Company merged they built a link to the Trent and Mersey Canal in 1833 so as to give direct access to Manchester. In 1835, the Birmingham and Liverpool Junction Canal gave traffic from the Ellesmere Canal a direct route to the West Midlands and the south. Even after the arrival of locomotive railways, canal projects continued to be completed.

By 1850, Britain had improved 680 miles of river navigations and built 4,000 miles of canals. Efficient inland waterway transport reached into all the principal industrial areas of the country.

A boat crosses Chirk aqueduct

Ellesmere Port
and the National Waterways Museum

Ellesmere Port was the new port created by the Ellesmere Canal Company at the northern terminus of its canal system on the Mersey estuary. The estuary carried traffic downstream to the great Atlantic port of Liverpool and upstream through various river navigations and canals to Manchester and south Lancashire. The canal company took over a wharf at Whitby near Netherpool and opened its first section of the canal to link this to Chester in 1796. The port was planned by William Jessop and Thomas Telford. Wide locks were built from the canal down into the estuary. In the 1830s Telford masterminded further development to include piers, basins, locks and multi-storey warehouses arched majestically over canal arms. A report in 1843 said:

> A few years since, there were upon this site but a public-house, three small cottages, an excuse for a warehouse, and one set of locks. Now it has upwards of seventy houses … a church, schools, two or three inns, two sets of locks; a splendid and most ample range of warehouses, erected on arches over various branches of the canal … besides the vast new dock.

The docks handled imports to send back along the Ellesmere Canal and traffic to and from other canals in the midlands and south. Passenger services went regularly to Liverpool. Boatbuilding businesses grew up and other industries established themselves around the port in the succeeding generations, including flour milling, chemical processing and car making. The port was improved by the arrival of the Manchester Ship Canal in 1891.

Although the great arched warehouses were destroyed by fire, much of the docks remains and is home to the **National Waterways Museum** and its fleet of historic boats, equipment, images and archives. Now run by the Canal & River Trust, the museum complements the Trust's other museums at Gloucester Docks and Stoke Bruerne.

Ellesmere Port and Telford's warehouses

The designers

It was a feat of extraordinary skill to thread a level pound of water for miles through any landscape, let alone through the valleys and hills of the Welsh borders. Making the canal safe, easy to maintain and suited to large amounts of traffic provided further challenges. With so many canals being built at the same time around Britain, improved techniques and practical solutions were being discovered and developed with each new project. Engineers with experience of the latest methods were in short supply.

William Jessop (page 28) was one of the engineers in greatest demand. He was the most prolific designer of the canal age, working on many different schemes at once around the country. He was revered by his contemporaries. The Ellesmere Canal Company appointed Jessop as their consulting engineer and he laid out the route that was first decided on, assisted by William Turner, John Duncombe and Thomas Denson.

In October 1793, with construction already underway, Thomas Telford (page 29) was appointed as 'General Agent, Surveyor, Engineer, Architect and Overlooker for the Works'. His roles were to submit detailed drawings to Jessop for amendment and approval and to oversee the work as it was carried out. Telford was already based in Shropshire, where he continued to work as county surveyor at the same time. He was thirty-six years old and he had no experience of waterways. His work on the Ellesmere Canal was a turning point in his career – a first opportunity to tackle a huge engineering project. Over the next few years he was to become the most famous and influential engineer of his generation.

Jessop and Telford were a powerful combination: Jessop experienced in canal-building, able to shoulder the responsibility for radical decisions, wise and practical; Telford fascinated by the latest technologies, with an eye for robust good design, and with great aptitudes in organisation. In his speech at the opening of Pontcysyllte aqueduct, the Ellesmere Canal Company chairman Rowland Hunt praised

... our General Agent, Mr Telford, who with the advice and judgement of our eminent and much respected Engineer Mr Jessop, invented and with unabating diligence carried the whole into execution.

It is hard to imagine either of the two men achieving what they did at Pontcysyllte without the other. They were also both highly capable in the art of building an effective team to support them. The project became a model of professional roles and responsibilities shared between specialist team members, which was to become normal engineering practice in future. The hand-picked team included Matthew Davidson as inspector of works, master stonemasons John Simpson and John Wilson, ironmaster William Hazledine, and William Davies responsible for the great earthworks. With the exception of Davies, all went on to work on Telford's other major projects, both in Britain and abroad.

'Among the boldest efforts of human invention in modern times', J. Phillips, 1803

The challenging territory through which the canal was taken is clear from the air. It crosses steep slopes through Chirk Bank on the left, then crosses the valley in the distance by Chirk aqueduct and tunnels under the hill beyond the town of Chirk. The huge modern road viaduct in the foreground gives a sense of scale

William Jessop (1745 – 1814)

William Jessop was born in 1745. He was the son of Josias Jessop, a foreman shipwright in the naval dockyard at Devonport who was responsible for the maintenance of the wooden lighthouse on Eddystone Rock. When the lighthouse burnt down in 1755, the great engineer John Smeaton designed a new one in stone – Josias oversaw the building work and they developed a close friendship. Smeaton was guardian and tutor to the teenage William Jessop after his father died in 1761, and he took him on as his assistant for several years. Jessop became one of the early members and then secretary of the Society of Civil Engineers, which was founded by Smeaton in 1771 as the first professional body for 'civil' as distinct from military engineering.

William Jessop, in a portrait by George Dance

When appointed to the Ellesmere Canal in 1791 Jessop was forty-six and the dominant canal engineer in Britain. He had already worked on the Grand Canal of Ireland and the Cromford Canal. He was an authority on the structural use of iron and in 1790 he had been a founding partner in the Butterley iron company in Derbyshire. Soon after starting work on the Ellesmere Canal he was responsible for the West India Docks in London, the massive floating harbour in Bristol, the Surrey Iron Railway and the Grand Junction Canal, which linked the Midlands directly with London. He also worked with Telford on the Caledonian Canal in Scotland. The Edinburgh Encyclopaedia said of Jessop in a biographical article three years after his death,

> Totally free of all envy and jealousy of professional rivalship, his proceedings … were free from all pomp and mysticism, and persons of merit never failed in obtaining his friendship and encouragement.

Thomas Telford (1757 – 1834)

Thomas Telford achieved his success despite humble beginnings. He was born the son of a shepherd in lowland Scotland and aged thirteen was apprenticed as a stonemason. After working in Edinburgh, London and Portsmouth he moved to Shrewsbury in 1786 to practise as a self-taught architect. In 1787 he was appointed County Surveyor for Shropshire, responsible for the county's bridges and buildings.

With his appointment to the Ellesmere Canal in 1793, Telford developed his knowledge of waterways and the use of iron in construction. In 1795 he designed an iron bridge across the river Severn at Buildwas and approved the construction in iron of the Longdon aqueduct for the Shrewsbury Canal. He went on to design the most modern

An engraved portrait of Telford in 1796, after the painting by Henry Raeburn

and efficient waterways of the canal age, carrying forward approaches pioneered by Jessop, in waterways such as the Caledonian Canal in Scotland (with Jessop himself), the Birmingham Canal main line and the Birmingham and Liverpool Junction Canal. From 1808 to 1829 he advised on the 118-mile Göta Canal in Sweden. He took part in the building or improvement of over 100 harbours.

Telford was responsible for building over 900 miles of roads and 1,000 bridges, including the Holyhead Road linking London and Dublin (page 87) and the majestic Menai suspension bridge, which was seen as one of the wonders of the age when it was completed in 1826. He became known in his own time as 'Pontifex Maximus', the 'Greatest of all Bridge-builders', and was honoured as a Fellow of the Royal Society and first President of the Institution of Civil Engineers.

The navvies

Canals were known as 'navigations' and the men who built them 'navigators' or 'navvies'. At the end of the eighteenth century there were probably 50,000 navvies building canals in Britain. In 1804, about 500 were in work at Pontcysyllte completing the main line and beginning the branch to Llangollen. Some attended the procession of boats to open Pontcysyllte aqueduct, after which the Chairman of the Canal Company recalled:

Navvies' tools

'Our honest friends the workmen, who had laboured hard for years in the undertaking, were regaled in their favourite manner, and were hailing our approach with honest jollity ...'

As well as digging with spade and barrow they built walls, planted hedgerows, puddled clay in the canal bed and blasted through rock. It was estimated that in good soil, an experienced navvy could shift 9 cubic metres of earth a day and twenty-five men could dig a mile of canal a year – but tunnels, embankments or cuttings (especially through rock) were slower.

People rarely thought the navvies worthy of mention, except to complain about rowdy behaviour and drinking. Even the poet Robert Southey merely likened them to ants on an ant-hill. Some would have been local labourers, farm workers or tradesmen such as carpenters, bricklayers and masons. Many moved around the country from one canal project to the next and lived in temporary encampments and barracks or lodged with local families. When the tunnel and cuttings at Chirk were being built in 1801, the census recorded 339 labourers and extractive industry workers in the parish and only one house uninhabited – Llangollen, by contrast, where there was no canal-building at the time, had about 89 labourers and 20 empty houses.

The navvies' work continued through the nineteenth century building railways and other engineering projects: in 1845 there were said to be 200,000 of them. In the 1880s Mrs Garnett of the Navvy Mission Society, which aimed to improve their conditions, said:

Certainly no men in all the world, so improve their country as Navvies do England. Their work will last for ages, and if the world remains so long, people will come hundreds of years hence to look at and to wonder at what they have done.

Building the canal

How did the canal builders work? Once the line was set out, sections were chosen to begin, detailed designs were done and contracts were let. Skilled craftsmen and gangs of navvies flooded in and began preparing materials, digging, moving earth and building. Work started in the 11 miles of the World Heritage site in 1795 at Chirk Bank with contracts for the terraced cutting and embankment along the side of the Ceiriog valley. The canal came into use in sections: to Chirk basin in 1801, Froncysyllte in 1802, Trevor in 1805 and Llangollen in 1808. Work was also done on the abandoned northern route of the canal north-west of Wrexham (page 47).

The steep slopes and valleys to be crossed presented many challenges but the Ellesmere Canal maintained a level and remarkably direct route compared with the flights of locks and diversions on many earlier canals (in fact, there is not a single lock in the World Heritage site). The engineers cut through rising ground and crossed valleys, using tunnels and cuttings, high embankments, and the innovative aqueducts at Chirk and Pontcysyllte, the ideas for which evolved even as the canal was being built. When it was completed, this extraordinary part of the canal was said to be 'composed of works more difficult of execution than can perhaps be found anywhere within an equal distance of canal navigation'.

The channel and water control

The basic requirement was the water channel. This was dug by navvies using picks and shovels and wheelbarrows on runs of planks. Typically, it had a level centre section 1m deep that sloped gently up under the water on either side. A flat towpath was made on one side for the horses that drew the boats. Hedges were planted to separate the towpath from farmland, with oak trees that could be harvested when timber was needed in future. The bed was waterproofed with a layer of compacted ('puddled') clay, except where the ground was natural clay or impermeable rock. The main line was built mostly to a width of about 9.2m, enough to allow boats to pass easily, but sometimes less on embankments and in cuttings. The Llangollen branch was narrower, typically about 8m wide, and with more sub-standard sections as it lay on steep slopes and was not expected to carry heavy traffic.

Part of the Llangollen branch near Trevor in 1936, showing the wide towpath and the trees planted in the hedgerow

The elegant curving weir at Horseshoe Falls

Reliable and plentiful sources of water were essential. Busy canals could have traffic interrupted by water shortages. As the first parts of the Ellesmere Canal were built it relied on capturing nearby streams. Jessop had planned to build a reservoir at the highest level of the canal and take water from the river Clywedog west of Wrexham. In 1795 he also proposed the river Dee above Llangollen as a water source and improvements far upstream at Llyn Tegid (Lake Bala) to enable it to operate as a reservoir (page 138). After the northern route was abandoned, the Llangollen feeder became essential. It was designed by Telford and Thomas Densen with Jessop's oversight and built between 1804 and 1808. The scheme included a curving weir at Horseshoe Falls near Llantysilio (page 136) and the improvements at Bala.

Sometimes water had to be let out of the canal as well as in. Overflows and sluices were built to help lengthsmen control the level and avoid flood damage. These vital features varied in form from simple sluice gates set in the towpath to elegant overflow weirs. Although easily overlooked, many were built with great craftsmanship and attention to detail so as to prevent erosion of the earthworks. Among commonplace features along the canal are grooves facing one another across the canal in the stonework of bridges. These were where wooden 'stop-planks' could be inserted to dam up the water if there was sudden damage to a bank or if a section needed to be drained.

Rack and pinion gear for opening a sluice under the towpath to let water out of the canal

Bridges

The channel had to be crossed in numerous places. Over-bridges had to be built to carry roads across the canal, provide access for traders or accommodate landowners whose property was divided by the new waterway. Telford and Jessop resisted building bridges on the busy main line where possible, as they would be bottlenecks to traffic. Nevertheless, twenty-three bridges built at the same time as the canal survive in the 11 miles of the World Heritage site, nineteen of which are virtually unaltered. The original over-bridges were of several types to suit different situations.

The 'standard' bridges follow the traditional form found on British canals: sweeping, hump-backed bridges with single spans wide enough for a single boat and the towpath. However, Telford's training as a stonemason gave them special elegance. The standard design was altered to suit local circumstances, in particular the lie of the land and the available materials – stone varied according to local availability, and brick was used for some wider arch rings or even whole bridges.

Among the innovative features of the canal were four over-bridges of composite construction – masonry strengthened with curving cast-iron beams. These enabled Telford to lay a flattened arch and reduce the slopes of the approaches, something particularly important for public road crossings.

Some timber draw-bridges were also built, where a crossing needed to be made at low level. These had large overhead beams with, at one end, a wooden box filled with stone as a counterbalance. With the help of a boatman pulling a rope, the beam would tip and chains from the opposite end would pull up one end of the bridge deck. (These have now all been replaced with safer modern versions.) At several locations Telford installed elegant timber footbridges standing on stone piers with staircases up at either end.

Stop-planks were inserted to dam up sections of canal for maintenance. The grooves for placing them are often under bridges

A flat stone arch supported by iron beams at Trevor basin

The small bridge over the water feeder at Tŷ Craig

A bridge on a slope at Bryn-ceirch

A wide arch to accommodate a curve at Millars bridge

Llanddyn draw bridge

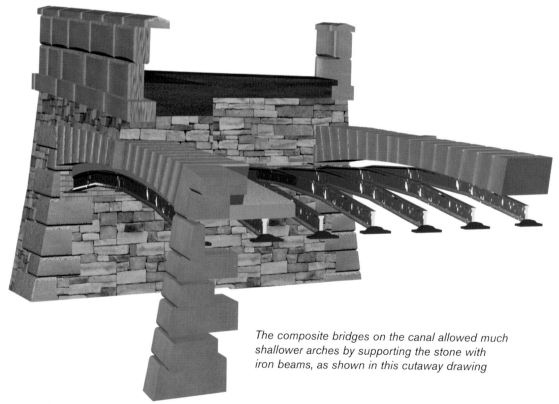

The composite bridges on the canal allowed much
shallower arches by supporting the stone with
iron beams, as shown in this cutaway drawing

The cuttings around Chirk were planted with trees to consolidate their sides

Cuttings and embankments

Cuttings and embankments were needed on a great deal of the canal. Jessop had long experience of excavating and depositing earthworks effectively and securely. He and Telford made sure that sides were sloped to safe gradients and planted with trees to consolidate them and that deposited material was layered and compacted to reduce the potential for later settlement. Telford's development of cut-and-fill calculations economised on the effort of moving large amounts of earth and enabled material excavated from one place to be taken to where it would be most needed.

Small cuttings were used in many places to pass slightly higher ground without going around it. The grandest cuttings were those near Chirk, where the larger ridge between the Dee and Ceiriog valleys was cut through up to 10m deep. The work was costly and intensive but the alternative to this route would have been a loop three or four times longer.

Free-standing embankments were built to cross valleys and depressions. The largest was the 27.5m-high earthwork leading to Pontcysyllte aqueduct (page 99), which was probably the largest civil earthwork of the eighteenth century in Britain. It was one of the first engineering projects in which temporary railways were used systematically to move materials. Telford recorded in a report of 1804: 'The Earthen Embankment and Lining for the Canal, is carrying on by means of three Iron Railways.' Where spoil had to be taken to the top of a cutting, horse-powered barrow inclines were created.

The enormous wooded embankment approaching Pontcysyllte seen from the air in winter

Terraces along steep slopes had to be built wherever the canal was perched on a valley side. These were made of cuttings on one side and embankments on the other. The greatest example was at Chirk Bank, which led for 0.7 miles to Chirk aqueduct (page 78).

In places where a watercourse had to be taken safely under the earthworks, culverts were built of sturdy rubble masonry. Many embankments needed them. The longest on the canal passed for 100m under the platform on which Trevor basin was built.

Although they are seldom noticed, many fine culverts were built to carry watercourses under the canal. This one is at Trevor Mill

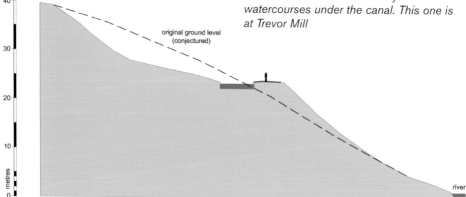
A cross section through the huge terrace embankment at Chirk

The tunnels

Tunnels are also an important feature of the World Heritage site. While earlier canals had driven tunnels through obstacles that were unavoidable, Telford and Jessop used them to shorten the route, breaking through higher ground that earlier canals would have gone around. The very long tunnel on the abortive Ruabon line of the canal was never begun, but the engineers built two shorter tunnels near Chirk (pages 86–94), as well as another near Ellesmere. Britain had around 36 miles of canal tunnels by the time that the network reached its peak in the mid-nineteenth century – far more than the total in the rest of the world at that time, as few tunnels of great length had yet been built outside Britain.

The Ellesmere Canal's tunnels are lined with brick and wide enough to take a towpath

The high retaining wall and entrance to Chirk tunnel

For the construction, Telford followed a cut-and-cover technique where possible – digging a trench and then building an arch over it before backfilling to the surface – so as to build safely and strongly. He and Jessop also gave their tunnels towpaths, which made them far quicker and easier for boats to pass through than the earlier tunnels where boats had to be 'legged' by men who pushed the boat along by walking on the walls or roof. Chirk was only the second canal tunnel in Britain to have a towpath – the first was at Berwick on the nearby Shrewsbury Canal just four years earlier.

The aqueducts

The World Heritage site is famous above all for its two great aqueducts. The development of the engineers' ideas for them is a twelve-year story of overcoming huge challenges by pioneering new techniques.

The engineers built two conventional aqueducts between Gledrid and Llangollen, one over the river Eglwyseg at Pentrefelin (page 132) and one over a track at Cross Street (page 95). Both were built in stone with a mass of puddled clay to waterproof the channel. The bulkiness of these structures hints at the difficulties and expense of using such techniques on a much larger scale. Several such aqueducts had failed on other canals during the 1790s and Jessop himself was encountering difficulties with aqueducts distorted by the instability of the puddled clay. The height and length needed to cross the valleys at Chirk and Pontcysyllte meant that the engineers had to think about the problem in completely new ways.

William Jessop had always advised crossing the valleys at full height. However, by the time that Telford was appointed in 1793, the proprietors of the canal had agreed to a cheaper and more cautious solution at Pontcysyllte – embankments at a lower level and a three-span aqueduct over the river. The reduced height would be made possible by flights of locks down on either side.

This was a poor compromise as water from the canal in both directions would be wasted and the canal might not be able to cope with the volume of traffic expected. However, the engineers thought again when the growing enthusiasm for the potential of the industrial material of cast iron brought new life to the high-level crossing. If iron was used it might make a cheaper and more practical structure, without thick walls and unstable puddled-clay. On 14 July 1795, Jessop reported, 'I must now recommend to the Committee to make this saving by adopting an Iron Aqueduct at the full height originally intended …'. He proposed a cast-iron trough on eight stone piers, 50 feet (15.2m) apart.

Chirk aqueduct was the tallest navigable aqueduct in the world when it was completed in 1801, though it was later overshadowed by Pontcysyllte aqueduct and by the railway viaduct beside it

The conventional, stone-built aqueduct at Pentrefelin

Since the opening of the inspirational Iron Bridge at Coalbrookdale in 1781 there had been a flowering of confidence in the possibilities of cast iron among a group of engineers and ironmasters familiar with one another's work, including William Reynolds and 'iron mad' John Wilkinson, who were both influential in the Ellesmere canal company. The Pontycafnau iron aqueduct had been built for a water-power channel and a tramroad at Merthyr Tydfil in about 1793. This was seen by William Reynolds and he and Thomas Eyton proposed an iron aqueduct on the Shrewsbury Canal in March 1795, after the stone one under construction had been destroyed by floods. This was to be designed by Telford as the engineer newly appointed to replace the Shrewsbury Canal's original engineer, who had died before the project was completed. At exactly the same time Jessop and his business partner Benjamin Outram were building a small iron aqueduct on the Derby Canal. In March 1795 the American inventor Robert Fulton, who was working

with Outram, proposed that iron should be used for the Marple aqueduct on the Peak Forest Canal – this was not followed through but a year later Fulton published an engraving of a design for an iron aqueduct in his *Treatise on the Improvement of Canal Navigation*.

On 25 July 1795 the foundation stone at Pontcysyllte was laid. During 1796 Telford prepared detailed specifications and sought tenders for the iron components. Work at Chirk was continuing in tandem, where in June 1796 the foundation stone was laid for stone piers to carry an iron superstructure. But suddenly the plans were put into doubt. The aqueduct completed on the Shrewsbury Canal at Longdon on Tern in March 1796 showed worrying signs of distorting with the weight of the water. As a result, the time may have not seemed right for all-iron troughs on the two largest aqueducts ever to have been built. Telford altered the Chirk designs to use stone arches. In 1799, work at Pontcysyllte was suspended while Chirk was completed.

Chirk aqueduct strides across the Ceiriog valley

Important innovations were pursued at Chirk by waterproofing without puddled clay. Instead, the trough was made from cast-iron plates at the base and high-fired brickwork pointed with hydraulic lime at the sides. The arches were built with hollow cross walls rather than solid fill above them to reduce the weight on the foundations, and these supported the iron bed plates directly. The engineers also seem to have developed a system of using temporary gangways to bring materials across the structure as it grew – a technique that was developed at Pontcysyllte.

While they were learning lessons at Chirk, Jessop and Telford developed their plans for the even more demanding challenge of the Dee valley. Construction of the abutments and piers at Pontcysyllte restarted early in 1800. The weight of the piers was minimised by tapering them as they rose and leaving hollow upper sections with strengthening cross-walls. Jessop pointed out that 'it will save five or six hundred pounds in the expence; and what to me appears most material, it will afford safety to the workmen'. A debate had begun about whether it would be cost-effective to build a tramroad across the piers rather than a canal, but in November 1801 the committee resolved that the canal should cross to Trevor. Telford commissioned a wooden model of one span (now conserved in the collections of the Canal & River Trust). In March 1802 a contract was signed with William Hazledine to supply the ironwork and fix it in place. By November 1804 the arches and trough had been completed over nine spans. The aqueduct opened in 1805.

The whole of the Ellesmere Canal and its branches as completed had cost some £500,000 to build. Of this, the two great aqueducts at Chirk and Pontcysyllte had cost £20,898 and £38,499 respectively. (Judged by wage inflation since 1800, £38,000 would be worth about £39 million today.)

The daring 'canal in the air'

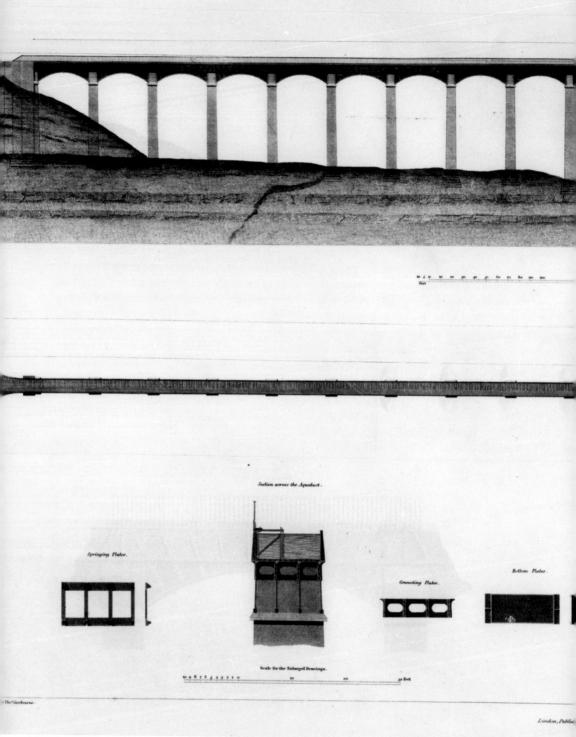

Pontcysyllte aqueduct as shown in Telford's atlas of his own work, published in 1838

Elevation of one Arch &c.

Tramroads

Under their Acts of Parliament many canals had powers to build linking railways up to 8 miles long. Although horse-worked 'tramroads' could not carry as much as the canal, they were cheaper to build, they could reach into higher ground, and branches could be laid quite quickly wherever needed. Tramroads were gently graded. As most traffic was coming from places higher than the canal, horses could easily take down full trains and pull back the empty wagons. In some cases the downward traffic ran just by gravity. Tramroads could also deal with very steep drops by using 'inclines' or 'inclined planes' to raise and lower wagons from a winding drum at the top. Some tramroads were laid with edge-rails that took flanged wheels, like a modern railway, but many were 'plateways', which had L-shaped rails and plain wheels. Track was laid onto iron tie bars, wooden sleepers, or stone blocks, which can still be found as evidence of the old routes.

From the basin at Trevor, the Ruabon Brook or Pont Cysyllte railway, which had been built in the 1790s to bring materials to construct the aqueduct, was extended to quarries, ironworks, collieries and clay-pits around Cefn Mawr, Acrefair, Ruabon, Pen y Cae and Rhosllanerchrugog. It was a busy route with double track. Much of it was converted into a standard-gauge railway with steam locomotives in the 1860s. Its course is followed by streets in Cefn Mawr (page 116) and Rhosllanerchrugog. By 1815 a plateway (later an edge-railway) with inclines connected Froncysyllte limestone quarries to canal-side limekilns (page 97–8). Nearby at Pen-y-graig there were five inclines from the quarries and other tramroads went to the Eglwyseg limestone outcrops (page 122–3). By 1817 a tramroad went from the canal north of Chirk to Black Park colliery and in 1825 a railway brought coal from Quinta colliery to Gledrid bridge.

Several later railways also joined the canal, even after main-line railways had come to the area. The Oernant tramway opened in 1857 for 4.5 miles from Pentrefelin through one long incline to the slate quarries at Oernant, Berwyn and Moel y Faen. A tramway to Pen-y-bont clay works operated from the 1860s. The Glyn Valley horse-operated tramway was built in 1873 to link slate and granite quarries at Glynceiriog to the canal at Gledrid before miniature Beyer Peacock locomotives were introduced in 1888–9 and the line was diverted to Chirk station and the canal at Chirk. A group aims to restore part of it.

A reconstructed section of horse-worked tramroad in Blaenavon

The lost canal and patent lift

Until 1800 the canal company still hoped to build its route northward from Pontcysyllte. It was intended to follow the contour around the south of the Cefn Mawr ridge (roughly on the line of the later Plas Kynaston canal) and to rise 76 feet (23m) through locks. It was then to turn north past Ruabon and Bersham and fall by many locks to Gresford and Chester. Among several planned branches was one to Ffrwd and Brymbo, of which over 2 miles were dug in 1796. Some dry sections can still be found near Ffrwd.

Somewhere in this area an extraordinary experimental lift was tried out as an alternative to locks. It was the brainchild of Exuperius Pickering and another canal shareholder, Edward Rowland. They registered a patent in 1794 under the title 'Invention of an improved Method of constructing navigable Canals, without the Use of Locks or inclined Planes, whereby most of the Objections to, and Inconveniences arising from, Canals are effectually removed'. Locks interrupted traffic and used a lot of water, which was often in short supply if canals were high up. The canal company agreed that Pickering and Rowland could build a trial somewhere convenient to the route, and if it worked well they would pay for it.

The lift was completed in 1796 and demonstrated over the next few years. The prototype rose about 12 feet (3.7m), slightly more than most locks, but Pickering and Rowland believed they could lift boats up to 100 feet (30m). A well below the bottom level of the canal contained a huge airtight timber float. This supported a tall structure topped with a tank of water to take a boat. The float moved up and down through the well aided by gears, and the tank containing the boat was lifted with it, supported by walls and guide rails. Tightly-fitting gates held the water in the tank and the canal above. The lift seems to have worked reasonably well. However, in 1800 the company reimbursed the inventors only a quarter of its cost of £800. No longer on the route, it was abandoned. So far, attempts to find whatever of this mysterious experiment may remain buried have been without success.

At Anderton in Cheshire a much later lift, built in 1875 to join the river Weaver to the Trent and Mersey Canal, is kept in working order by the Canal & River Trust. Even more modern is the Falkirk Wheel in Scotland, which opened in 2002.

The successful lift at Anderton, built three generations after the trial for the Ellesmere Canal

Reactions and influences

The canal made a powerful impression on people's imaginations. Visitors when it was newly built considered it a work of art and a masterpiece of human ingenuity. Chirk aqueduct was praised even before it was finished – the antiquarian Sir Richard Colt Hoare wrote that 'from the length of this building, the straight lines and light piers which intersect the valley it has a pleasing effect even in its imperfect state. When finished it will have the most grand and picturesque appearance.'

Numerous drawings and engravings were produced of Pontcysyllte aqueduct, emphasising above all its delicacy against the backdrop of wild scenery. The Scottish novelist Sir Walter Scott declared it 'the most impressive work of art I have ever

Pontcysyllte aqueduct was celebrated in a print after John Parry published in 1806, the year after it was completed

seen' and the American writer Washington Irving called it 'stupendous'. Engineers and scientists were equally impressed. In 1816, the French engineer Charles Dupin called it 'something enchanted', 'a supreme work of architecture, elegant and unadorned'. The scientist Michael Faraday crossed the aqueduct in 1819, noting that it was 'too grand a thing to be hastily passed'.

The skills of British canal engineers were sought overseas as a result of their success. Jessop's professional reputation resulted in contact with canal promoters from many countries. In the twenty years from 1808 Telford advised on canal projects in Nova Scotia, India, Russia and Sweden. The engineers of the Ellesmere Canal constantly revised their ideas in the light of experience, turning the canal into a testing ground for engineering and business practice. Approaches to design that were carried forward afterwards included the bold engineering of routes that commanded the landscape, the use of iron, towpaths in canal

tunnels and functionalism in architectural form. In terms of construction methods, the use of temporary railways to move materials and the use of cut-and-fill calculations to ensure the efficient movement of spoil were important for the future. Organisational developments included the division of responsibility between specialists, principles of contract management and consideration of safety for workers (page 100).

Britain's new industrial transport system drew statesmen, entrepreneurs and engineers from many parts of Europe and America to see it for themselves. In 1817, the American engineer Canvass White was sent to Europe by the New York State Governor to study canal construction. He walked 2,000 miles along British canals and returned with notes, drawings and instruments that assisted his own work on the Erie Canal. In 1818, Francois Becquet, the director of France's Bureau des Ponts et Chausées, sent three engineers to Britain to study canals. One of them was J. M. Dutens who travelled 1,800 miles of canals and made detailed drawings of the chain bridge above Llangollen (page 134). His investigations resulted in an influential report to the King of France proposing a comprehensive network of canals in the manner of the British system but on a yet larger scale. Many publications in Britain and overseas, too, disseminated what had been learned from the British canals.

The Caledonian Canal in Scotland, built from 1803 to 1822, was one of the great projects that Jessop and Telford went on to design elsewhere. It was capable of carrying ocean-going ships © RCAHMS

An open working boat without a cabin

Operating the canal

The canal was managed by the Ellesmere Canal Company and its committees from its Ellesmere headquarters (page 53). The company employed lengthsmen and labourers to take care of particular sections and toll-keepers to collect the tolls for the goods that boats were carrying. Most maintenance workers lived in neighbouring communities but some cottages were provided for key workers.

Financially, the canal was not so successful for its investors as some had been, owing to the high cost of building in such a challenging landscape and the financial difficulties of the period, when Britain was involved in a lengthy war with France and costs were rising rapidly. However, toll income increased steadily and the company had no remaining debts within five years of the canal's completion. It was able to pay its shareholders dividends regularly from 1815 onwards and trade grew steadily for nearly half a century. Few new companies today could be relied on to have such long-term value.

Most of the boats that used the canal initially were owned by industrial companies or carriers, but the canal company also

Canal workers repairing the drained Montgomery Canal at Welshpool in about 1900

A classic narrow boat

operated a fleet and by the mid-nineteenth century its boats predominated. The canal was designed to carry the long, thin English canal craft. These 'narrow boats' were 22.1m long and 2.1m wide, built of timber, and could carry up to 20 tons of cargo (the size was limited by the locks). At full capacity, boats would ride low in the water, with only a few centimetres of the sides showing. The boats were drawn by horses using a rope from the towpath to a post just forward of the boat's mid-point (pulling a boat from the bow brings it into the bank). Typically there would be one person at the tiller to steer and another walking along with the horse. Some voyages would have been done in a day – for example taking coal to limekilns – but many went much further afield and would have required the crew to sleep under awnings on the boats. In the nineteenth century families began living permanently on board (page 65).

Goods and materials were brought to wharves – some provided by the canal company for the public and some owned by particular businesses – and put on board boats with the aid of gang-planks and cranes. There are remains of some twenty wharves and basins in the World Heritage site. Many appear simply as flat areas where slate, coal or lime were brought to the canal bank. A wharfinger might be responsible for the wharf and goods delivered there, sometimes using a weighbridge to check quantities. The wharves were often associated with a broadening of the canal into a basin or a boat turning point. At Froncysyllte, a large basin signifies that this was the terminus of the canal for three years before Pontcysyllte aqueduct was completed, and it continued to be an important place of interchange. The horse-worked tramroads that spread for miles from the wharves towards the mines, quarries and works ensured efficient delivery for industrial products. Many goods also arrived by roads and trackways.

Within two years of opening, the main line was carrying large cargoes of coal, limestone, timber, building stone, roofing slates, iron, brick and grain; and the volume of traffic doubled in the next decade. A trade directory of 1828 showed regular canal services through which people could send consignments to Chester, Manchester, Liverpool, Birmingham, Bristol, south Wales and London.

'It will have the effect, to create and establish a commercial intercourse and union between England and North Wales, by forming a navigable communication of the three rivers, Severn, Dee, and Mersey.'
The Universal Magazine, 1806

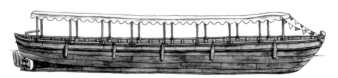

A horse-drawn pleasure boat

A 1950s cruiser

The Ellesmere Canal headquarters

The Ellesmere Canal Company had all its early meetings at the Royal Oak in the country town of Ellesmere, and during the building of the canal some of its staff lived there. Ellesmere was a natural point from which to administer the canal as it was more or less the central point on the main line as well as the place where the whole project had started (page 19). In 1805 the company decided to build its headquarters here. This fine building designed by Telford and now called Beech House still looks out over the junction between the canal and the short arm that went into Ellesmere itself. A curving committee room with great windows gave views along the canal in three directions, and there were accounts offices and engineers' offices. Just behind were a dry dock and storage building. Beech House remained the head office until 1846.

The canal company also built a maintenance yard to serve the canal at the head of the Ellesmere arm. It included a pattern store for iron objects needed on the canal, which were cast at a nearby foundry, carpenters' workshops, a saw-pit and a dry dock. Lock gates were made here, smiths hand-forged iron fittings, and boats were built and repaired. The yard is still used by the Canal & River Trust. Opposite it, on the east side of the canal arm, were public wharves and warehouses, a crane and a weighing machine. Just north of the wharves were the Duke of Bridgewater's iron foundry, timber yard and carpenters' shops.

The canal workshops and red-brick Beech House at Ellesmere

A modern holiday craft

The wealth of the nation: trades and industries

The great goal of the canal was to release the potential of mineral resources. At its opening it was said that the new waterway was 'destined to convey the riches of the mineral Kingdom into the World of Industry and thence to every part of the universe'. One immediate effect of cheaper transport by canal was that the price of coal fell across a wide area, thereby helping processing industries. Trades developed as people invested. Many new enterprises exported iron, coal, limestone and slate from the areas around Chirk, Trevor and Llangollen.

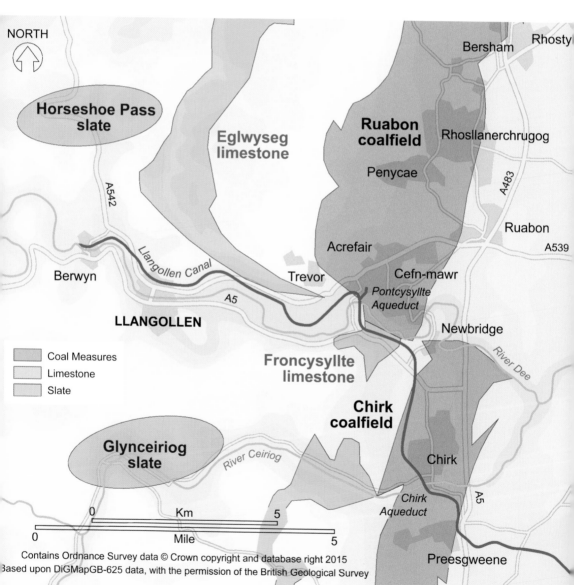

NORTH

Bersham · Rhosty

Horseshoe Pass slate

Eglwyseg limestone

Ruabon coalfield

Rhosllanerchrugog

Penycae

A542

A483

Ruabon

A539

Llangollen Canal

Acrefair

Berwyn

Trevor

Cefn-mawr

Pontcysyllte Aqueduct

A5

LLANGOLLEN

Newbridge

River Dee

Coal Measures
Limestone
Slate

Froncysyllte limestone

Chirk coalfield

Glynceiriog slate

River Ceiriog

Chirk

0   Km   5

0   Mile   5

Chirk Aqueduct

A5

Contains Ordnance Survey data © Crown copyright and database right 2015
Based upon DiGMapGB-625 data, with the permission of the British Geological Survey

Preesgweene

Coal mining

Coal fuelled the Industrial Revolution. When Pontcysyllte aqueduct opened in 1805, the inaugural procession included two empty boats that crossed the valley to be filled with coal at Trevor basin. Coal was difficult and costly to move over land, but canals could carry it easily and cheaply. By the nineteenth century, almost every industrial process used coal to power steam engines or to process materials, and growing towns depended on it for heating and cooking. Demand for it was increasing constantly. Thanks to the canal, the Denbighshire coalfield could supply nearby iron-making and lime-burning industries and extend the market for coal into Shropshire and Cheshire and up the Severn Valley to Montgomeryshire.

Small-scale coal pits existed in the area in the sixteenth century, producing small amounts of coal mainly for domestic use. The canal encouraged far greater investment. Black Park colliery near Chirk was one new development. Local businessman Thomas Edward Ward leased the small existing mine from the Chirk Castle estate in the year Pontcysyllte aqueduct was completed. Over the following twenty years he invested around £20,000 in improvements and built the Black Park collieries railway to his own loading dock in a spur off the canal (page 92). In the area north of Trevor basin, the Ruabon Brook railway connected a constantly increasing number of new mines to the canal.

A view of Acrefair by T. Walmsley in 1794 shows the wooden shaft gear at a small coal mine just as work on the canal was beginning. Mining expanded greatly after cheap transport was available

Left: The canal made it possible to exploit the mineral wealth of the area shown in this map. Most important were coal, iron ore and clay from the Ruabon and Chirk coalfields, limestone from Eglwyseg and Froncysyllte and slate from the Horseshoe Pass and Glynceiriog

Ironmaking

Iron was a material that was central to the Industrial Revolution. It was used to make everything from engineering structures to waterwheels and steam engines that powered industry, ships, machinery, rails, gates, horseshoes and nails. In 1838, the canal carried 22,000 tons of iron from the ironworks around Cefn Mawr to Liverpool and Manchester.

All the raw materials for making iron existed in large quantities in the area: coal, iron ore and limestone. Iron was made in a blast furnace by smelting iron ore with 'coke' (coal that had been roasted to drive off impurities). Limestone was added to help the iron separate from the waste slag. When the furnace was ready to tap, molten iron ran out into beds of sand as 'pig' iron or as cast-iron objects. The pigs could be cast again to make things in a foundry or further refined in a forge into 'wrought iron' for use in smiths' shops and forges. Improved transport allowed the pig iron and the products of foundries and forges in the area to be shipped to the rest of Britain.

The cast-iron parts for Pontcysyllte aqueduct were made at Plas Kynaston foundry by the ironmaster William Hazledine, very close to what was to become the head of the main line. Hazledine built the foundry in about 1800 to make the iron for the aqueduct, and he was awarded the contract in 1802. The canal enabled him to send large castings for engineering projects throughout Britain, and his works went on to supply iron for many of Telford's major projects, including the Göta Canal in Sweden and the Caledonian Canal and Craigellachie bridge in Scotland.

Newbridge iron furnace and forge were started to the south-east of Cefn Mawr at around the time the canal was being built. A tramroad was built to connect the works with sources of ironstone and coal. Another small iron forge, possibly with a blast furnace, was built by Exuperius Pickering junior alongside the canal at Trevor in about 1823.

The biggest local ironworks was at Acrefair. Edward Rowland established an ironworks there in 1817 that used the Ruabon Brook tramroad to carry goods to Trevor basin. In 1825 the British Iron Company bought this and the Newbridge works and continued to operate several blast furnaces, forges and rolling mills for making wrought-iron rails and bars. By the 1830s, a return supply of iron ore from Cumberland and other areas maintained the local industry when the local supplies of ore were running low. In 1854, the company was producing about 15,600 tons of iron a year, most of which was carried on the canal for sale to businesses in Manchester. At its peak the works employed over 1,500 people. Production ceased in 1887, and the only visible remains are some retaining walls and a bank of coke ovens near Lancaster Terrace in Acrefair.

The surviving retaining wall from the British Ironworks in Acrefair

Limestone quarrying

Limestone was not only used in the iron furnaces but burned in kilns to produce quicklime. Most importantly, this was spread on the land to improve acidic soils, resulting in better crops and pasture. Builders also used burnt lime for mortar and limewash, and it had many other applications as a chemical. Limestone was quarried in Denbighshire in the sixteenth century but new markets along the canal allowed quarries to expand enormously. When the Llangollen branch was being planned in 1803 it was part of its promotion that it would pass 'under the Trevor Lime Rocks'. By the mid-nineteenth century the canal regularly carried limestone to iron furnaces in the Black Country, some 70 miles away.

Pen-y-graig quarries at Froncysyllte are an example of the growth of limestone quarrying. By 1817, a tramroad incline connected a quarry high on the hillside with the canal. As it expanded, a complex system of tramroads developed to bring limestone

Limekilns beside the canal at Froncysyllte

to kilns next to the canal and the Holyhead Road, where it was burned using coal brought by boat. The quarries operated until 1954. The kilns and wharf can still be seen (page 97–8). Limekilns were built at many points on the canal to fulfil local demand. At the very head of navigation of the Llangollen branch Exuperius Pickering senior built a bank of limekilns at Tŷ Craig and a wharf for selling quicklime and coal (page 134).

Reconstruction drawing of a large bank of limekilns at Trevor cut away to show how they operated. Limestone and coal were brought to the top and burned quicklime was dragged out at the bottom

Industries around the Plas Kynaston Canal

Working limestone boats – detail from photograph on page 123

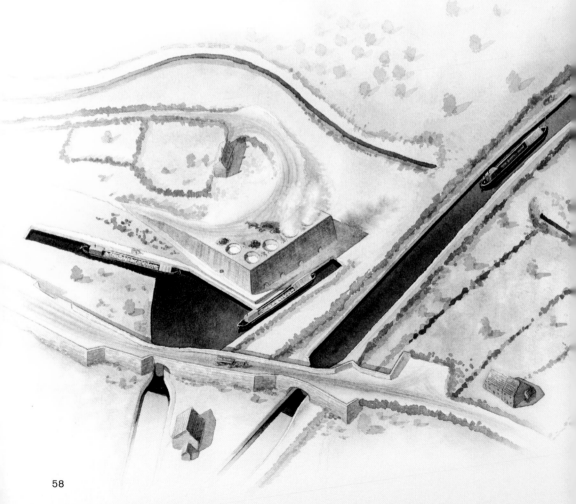

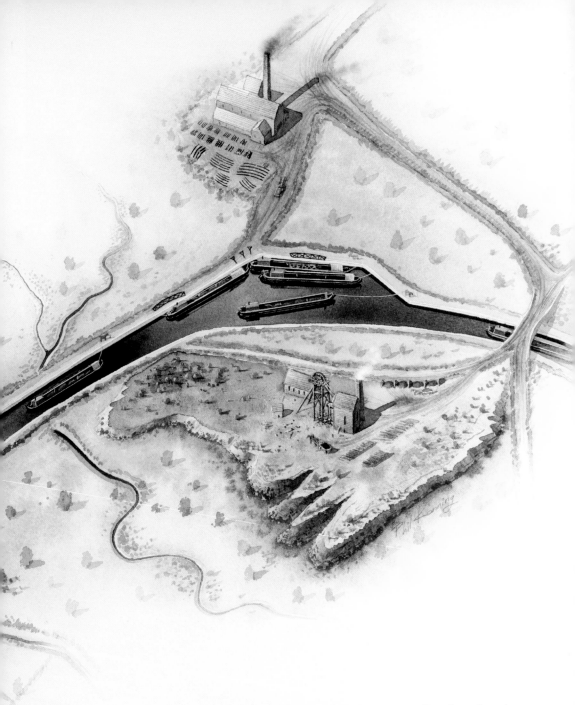

This drawing reconstructs how the Plas Kynaston Canal, starting at
the head of the main line at Trevor, might have looked in around 1870.
On the left is the earliest part of the canal, built around 1820 by
Exuperius Pickering, which brought limestone to a pair of docks
serving his limekilns. On the right is the extension of the canal
towards Cefn Mawr, built by Thomas Ward after 1829. This served
the Plas Kynaston iron foundry (at the top), a coal mine (right), and
further along a pottery and a chemical works. The canal was gradually
buried after about 1950 but there are ambitions to reopen it.

Clogau slate quarries and waste tips near the Horseshoe Pass

Slate quarrying

The canal served two slate-quarrying areas – one near the Horseshoe Pass and one at Glynceiriog. Slate was quarried around the Horseshoe Pass from the seventeenth century for roofing and building and taken to local markets in carts on rough tracks. However, after the arrival of the canal producers could bring slate down the valley to Pentrefelin and load it onto boats for markets as far away as Birmingham and Manchester. In the 1840s, a water-powered slate mill was built beside the canal (page 131) in which slabs were cut to size, split into smaller pieces and dressed to create a finished product. In 1857, the Oernant tramroad connected the slate quarries to the canal more efficiently and by 1858 they were producing around 6,000 tons a year.

The Glynceiriog quarries were also active before the construction of the canal and carted their slate to it, probably at Froncysyllte. They developed further after the Glyn Valley tramway was built in the 1870s, first joining the canal at Gledrid wharf and later at Chirk Bank.

Eglwyseg slate quarry 1881

Clay industries

Local clay pits, potteries and brick and tile makers took advantage of the canal to develop their business. Good quality clay was abundant in the coalfield. In the early nineteenth century, small-scale brickmaking and pottery production was found near the coal pits that provided fuel for the kilns. From the mid-nineteenth century, larger brickworks and potteries were developed in response to the increased demand for bricks, drains, floor tiles and decorative terracotta goods. The largest of the potteries was that of Bailey and Bradley at Plas Kynaston, which began making earthenware before 1818 and worked throughout the nineteenth century.

The most successful brick and tile works in the area were those of James Coster Edwards (1828–1896), a Denbighshire businessman who had operated a small brickworks at a coal mine owned by his father. In the 1860s, he acquired Tref-y-nant and Pen-y-bont clay works and began producing high-quality bricks, tiles and decorative terracotta in a distinctive bright red colour. Tramroads connected both works to the canal. Their products were used locally in houses, chapels and public buildings and were shipped to widespread markets: they

The Pierhead offices in Cardiff docks were built with terracotta made by J. C. Edwards in 1896–7

were used in a Royal Navy base in Singapore and buildings on the Panama and Suez canals. By around 1895 the two works had 69 kilns and employed 720 people. They operated until the mid-1950s but little remains of them today except for four brick gate piers at Tref-y-nant and a turreted lodge at Pen-y-bont. The products, however, can be seen throughout the area and in many other parts of the world.

Workers in front of the kilns at J. C. Edwards' Tref-y-nant terracotta works.
Many children worked at the factory.

Upper Dee Flannel Mills in Llangollen, which drove its machinery with water power from the canal

Building-stone quarrying

The piers of Pontcysyllte aqueduct were made from golden sandstone quarried nearby at Cefn Mawr (page 116). The quality of Cefn stone made it ideal for engineering structures, houses and industrial buildings. When the canal opened, the Ruabon Brook tramroad connected the quarries to Trevor basin and stone became a regular cargo. By 1845, in addition to the local trade by canal, about 1,000 tons a year were being carried as far as Liverpool.

Manufacturing chemicals

In 1867 Robert Graesser established a works alongside the Plas Kynaston branch canal north of Trevor basin to extract paraffin oil and wax from shale, a waste product of the local collieries. After a few years, demand for his products fell away owing to the availability of cheap supplies of oil from America, but Graesser developed processes to distil phenols and cresols from coal tar acids. The canal brought the materials from gasworks and took the products to their markets. The plant expanded, making dyes and an ingredient for explosives. Over half of Britain's phenol production was at Cefn Mawr until the 1890s when the United States and Germany came to dominate the world market, but Graesser's high-quality phenol continued to be in demand. The works by then used rail transport but it thrived supplying phenol for materials such as Bakelite, the world's first synthetic plastic, developed in 1907–9. After the First World War, the American chemical firm Monsanto bought into the works, which expanded onto the former Plas Kynaston foundry site. At its peak it had over 2,000 employees. In 1994, Monsanto combined with Akzo Nobel to form Flexys. The works closed in the early years of the twenty-first century.

Textiles

The mechanised production of woollen and cotton textiles for world-wide markets was one of the great achievements of the Industrial Revolution in Britain. A company from Manchester, Turner and Comber, opened cotton mills at Llangollen in around

1805 that were powered by water from the river Dee. Canal transport connected the mills to the larger centres of textile production in north-west England and to international markets.

The woollen industry – spinning wool and weaving woollen cloth – was a more established industry in Wales than cotton manufacturing at the time the canal was built. It continued to develop though its use of the canal may have been small. By 1820, some local woollen factories were producing up to 15,000 yards of material a week. In the mid-nineteenth century Upper Dee flannel mill was built at Llangollen driven by water from the canal. The last textile mills in Llangollen continued to work until the mid-twentieth century. Upper Dee Mill closed in about 1940 after almost ninety years of making woollen flannel.

Tourism

The canal began attracting tourists in its earliest years and continues to draw many thousands of visitors. People began to tour Wales in large numbers at the end of the eighteenth century, when war with France prevented British people taking the Grand Tour of Europe. Many travellers stopped at Pontcysyllte aqueduct and Llangollen on the way to Snowdonia. Early visitors included the Duke of Wellington and writers of the Romantic movement such as Shelley, Southey and Wordsworth. The north Wales tour continued to be popular in the nineteenth century, when among the visitors were the composer Felix Mendelssohn, the critic John Ruskin, the naturalist Charles Darwin and Queen Victoria.

In 1881, Mr Newbery of the Royal Hotel ran a timetabled pleasure boat from Llangollen wharf to the Chain Bridge and Captain Samuel Jones began a similar service with his boat *Maid of Llangollen* in 1884. By 1905, the service was running several times a day and went as far as Chirk every Wednesday. When the fast new railways brought more holidaymakers, such trips proved even more successful. Horse-drawn boat tours still go up the feeder from Llangollen wharf. The rest of the canal is busier than ever with tour boats and holiday craft.

Llangollen. Canal Walk.

One of the early pleasure boats on the canal at Pentre-felin sluice near Llangollen, pictured in a postcard of around 1900

The general trade wharf and warehouse at Llangollen

General trade

Although heavy industrial materials and products were the lifeblood of the canal, many other goods were carried too. Cargoes of grain were brought into the area to feed its growing population. Other agricultural crops were sent outward to the cities of the north-west. Oak timber was shipped for building work and bark was sent in large quantities for use in tanneries. Softwood poles and boards imported from northern Europe came back. Products flowed into the coalfield, where people of all classes had more spending power thanks to industrial growth. They bought tobacco, sugar, tea and coffee that came from the colonies, ceramics from Staffordshire, furniture, textiles of different

kinds from many parts of the world, and a huge diversity of other goods. A wharf at Ellesmere in 1834 advertised the enormous choice of imported materials it had for the building trades and associated uses:

R. & J. Tilston, who have constantly on sale, Memel, Riga, Dantzic, and Pine Balk; Norway, Scaffold and Ladder Poles; Red and White Deals, Laths, Slates, Tiles and Buckley Mountain Drainage Pipes, Wheelwrights and Coopers Stuff; Roman Cement; Boat Builders, Tarpawling, and Mill-sail Makers; and Vendors of Canvas, Rope, Pitch, Tar, etc.

The boat people

In the early years of the canal, most boatmen probably lived at home and sometimes spent a night or two sleeping on their boats. But as the British canal network grew, boatmen began to carry goods all over the country, sometimes with their families, who became referred to as 'boat people'. The number of boatmen continued to grow during the nineteenth century. By the middle of the century there were some 100,000 people living on Britain's waterways. In Froncysyllte there were 11 boat people on census night in 1841 and 20 in 1851. The 1881 census recorded only 6 boat people at Froncysyllte but 14 boats with crews living on board at Trevor basin and 12 near Llangollen. Most of the crews had been born at places on the Ellesmere Canal, but their children had been born at places across the Midlands. By the mid-nineteenth century, boats from the area travelled regularly to London with slate and limestone. The writer George Borrow spoke to a boatman near Llangollen around 1850:

> He told me that the canal and its branches extended over a great part of England. That the boats carried slates – that he had frequently gone as far as Paddington by the canal – that he was generally three weeks on the journey – that the boatmen and their families lived in the little cabins aft ... and that he liked no place so much as Llangollen.

The lives of children on the canal were challenging. The canal was less dangerous for children than working in mines, quarries or textile mills, but they often had accidents: reported examples included being kicked by a horse, drowning in the canal, crushing a hand in a crane, and being killed by falling wood at a wharf. In 1870, the Education Act aimed to ensure children went to school, and this posed problems for canal families on the move. John Williams, a School Attendance Officer from 1876 to 1883, reported:

> I have visited Froncysyllte and find a great many children who do not attend school ... there are several families at Froncysyllte where the father has a boat and he occasionally takes the whole family with him for a week. I have reasoned the matter over with them and the reply is that they cannot do otherwise.

Social commentators assumed poverty had forced boatmen to give up their homes and put their families to work. They noted the widespread illiteracy of boat people and believed they were living in misery. In 1873 George Smith wrote a book in which he argued that a canal boat was no place to bring up a family. His descriptions of cabins as 'filthy holes with bugs and vermin creeping up the sides' led to attempts to stop children living on board. However, the boat people disagreed and between 1885 and the 1920s various inspections found that in health, cleanliness, morality, feeding and clothing, they were the equals, if not the superiors, of town dwellers of a similar class.

A narrow-boat family waiting at the Black Park wharf in 1910. A tramway goes along the towpath. A small bridge crosses the entrance to the Black Park collieries' dock

From decline to World Heritage

The canals were eventually to be superseded by a dense national network of new railways that carried trains drawn by steam locomotives. The first of these railways were built into the Denbighshire coalfield from the late 1840s onwards. Trains could now compete with boats for traffic, but trade on the canal continued to increase. Industrial output and demand for transport were still growing. Many mines, quarries and factories had direct canal connections and would have found it difficult to change to the railways. Railways and canals could operate as complementary systems. The canal company itself invested in railways under a new identity as the Shropshire Union Railways and Canal Company as early as 1846.

However, business on the canal eventually did start to fall. In the early twentieth century the subsidiary Shropshire Union Canal Carrying Company was making a small profit but the increase in wages after the First World War wiped this away and it closed down in 1921. Other canal carriers who tried to continue the business also failed. The last recorded shipments in what is now the World Heritage site were coal from Black Park colliery in 1933 and stone for road building in 1935. Almost the whole of the canal was officially abandoned under an Act of Parliament in 1944. Many other parts of the British canal network closed at the same time.

An intrepid family of pleasure boaters exploring the canal in 1936, at one of the lift bridges

Meanwhile, campaigners were beginning to argue for the preservation of Britain's industrial heritage, canals included. Pontcysyllte aqueduct appeared in the film *Painted Boats* in 1945 (titled *The Girl of the Canal* in the United States). It became an iconic structure for the industrial heritage movement and especially for the Inland Waterways Association, which was set up in 1946 to press for the preservation and use of the canals. In 1949 one of the Association's founders, L. T. C. Rolt, battled his way along the canal in his boat *Cressy* to Trevor basin, where it had been built. In 1952, the Inland Waterways Association held a rally at Llangollen and the next year it formed a committee to campaign for the canal's revival.

When the British Waterways Board decided in 1954 to keep the canal open it was a victory for preservation and the recognition that waterways without industrial traffic nevertheless had public value. The Board contracted to supply water through the canal to north-west England and the payments largely covered the costs of keeping the canal open. It had been in danger of demolition just a few years earlier, but in 1958 Pontcysyllte aqueduct was designated a Scheduled Ancient Monument of National Importance.

In the late twentieth century, some unsympathetic approaches were taken to replacing stonework and timberwork, building new road crossings and lining the canal bed. However, improved techniques and greater awareness of historic character in the 1990s meant that the canal was cared for increasingly sympathetically. In 2003–4, British Waterways undertook an ambitious

A boat above the trees at Pontcysyllte

scheme of conservation at Pontcysyllte aqueduct ready for bicentenary celebrations in 2005. By 2007 nearly all the features in the 11-mile section of the canal from Gledrid to Llantysilio were either Listed Buildings or part of a Scheduled Ancient Monument and the whole group was nominated to become a World Heritage site.

In 2009, UNESCO inscribed Pontcysyllte Aqueduct and Canal on the World Heritage List. It judged it to be of 'outstanding universal value' as a masterpiece of engineering genius and a witness to transport development during the Industrial Revolution. The canal is now cared for by the Canal & River Trust and the World Heritage site is overseen by a partnership of local and national organisations.

Celebration at Pontcysyllte aqueduct for its bicentenary in 2005

Right: sun on the water at the Afon Bradley overflow near Chirk

Places to Visit

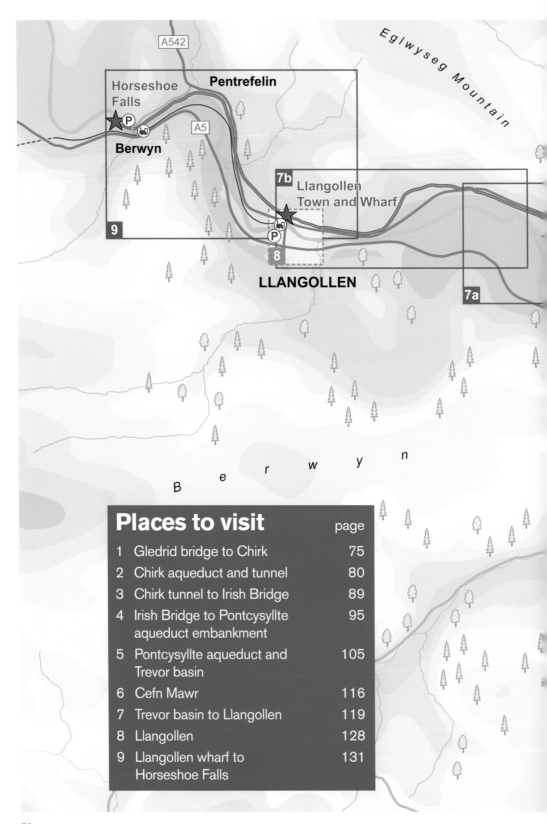

A542

Horseshoe Falls

Pentrefelin

Berwyn

A5

7b

Llangollen Town and Wharf

9

8

LLANGOLLEN

7a

Eglwyseg Mountain

B   e   r   w   y   n

Places to visit

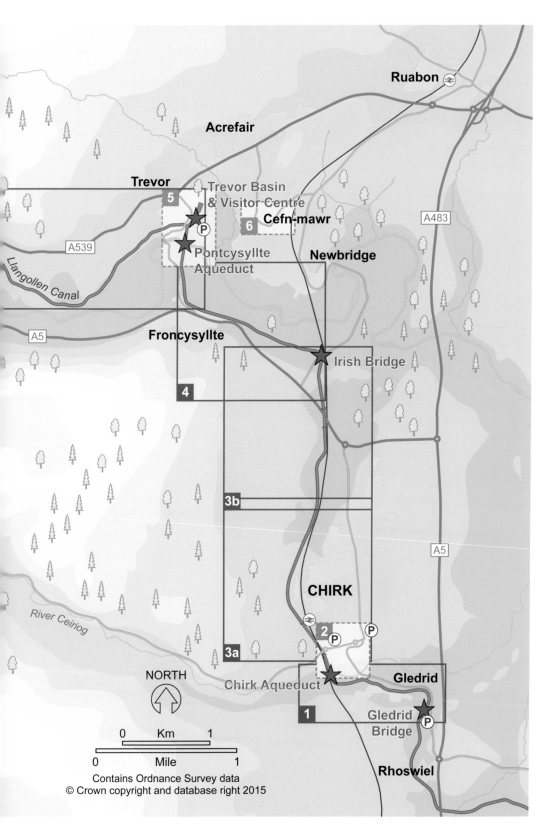

Ruabon

Acrefair

Trevor

5

Trevor Basin
& Visitor Centre

6 Cefn-mawr

A539

Newbridge

Pontcysyllte
Aqueduct

Llangollen Canal

A5

Froncysyllte

4

Irish Bridge

A483

3b

A5

CHIRK

River Ceiriog

3a

2

1

Chirk Aqueduct

Gledrid

Gledrid
Bridge

NORTH

Rhoswiel

0   Km   1

0   Mile   1

Contains Ordnance Survey data
© Crown copyright and database right 2015

73

This part of the guidebook helps you enjoy visits to the key features in and around the World Heritage site. A map of the site as a whole is on the previous page.

The text and maps follow the canal from east to west. You can use them to choose particular places to visit or find out more as you travel along the canal or its towpath. Conveniently placed car parks are shown on the maps. Features of interest are highlighted in **bold** and shown by numbers on the detailed maps. To help check where you are on the canal the text also gives the individual number of each bridge, which is shown on plates above the arches. Nearby sites of related interest are also mentioned, in the text or feature boxes.

If you have only a short time, the most important places to visit are Chirk aqueduct and tunnel (page 80), Pontcysyllte aqueduct (page 105) and Horseshoe Falls (page 131).

All of the canal towpath is level and easy to walk. Many sections are accessible for wheelchairs and pushchairs. The route from Trevor to Llangollen is particularly suitable.

For further information go to www.pontcysyllte-aqueduct.co.uk

During your visit be considerate towards others so that you and they can appreciate this special place. The canal and its towpath are working heritage. In places the towpath is narrow and the gap between the railings of the Pontcysyllte aqueduct is wider than you might expect. Look after your children, don't try to cycle across the aqueducts or through the tunnel and take the opportunity for contemplation.

Please take care for your safety when visiting and supervise children closely. Be aware of hazards, for example deep water, sudden drops, low headroom, road traffic and exposure.

Chirk

Gledrid bridge to Chirk

1 mile of level towpath. There is space to park cars near the canal at Gledrid bridge, next to the Poacher's Pocket pub. There is a car park near Chirk tunnel, at the Glyn Wylfa Centre and café on Castle Road (B4500) in Chirk.

The canal enters the World Heritage site at Gledrid in Shropshire. This is where the route began to encounter steep slopes and valleys that challenged the engineers to devise grander works. The canal is terraced on an enormous embankment against a hillside as it approaches the crossing of the Ceiriog valley.

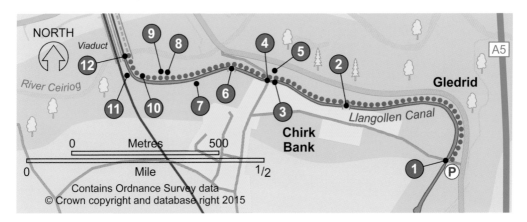

Gledrid bridge 19 ❶ is an original over-bridge built in about 1796 to the standard design. This one is built of brick, as the canal had not yet reached the supplies of good building stone a little further on. The towpath goes under the bridge, and there are grooves where wooden 'stop-planks' could be lowered to stop up the water. **Quinta Bridge ❷** further along the canal was demolished in the early twentieth century but the narrowing of the canal shows where it stood.

Gledrid bridge marks the entrance to the World Heritage site. It is one of very few standard bridges on the canal built of brick rather than stone

Canal View Cottages at Chirk Bank bridge, where there was once a wharf for transhipping goods between road and canal

A detail of one of the handful of bridges that used curved cast-iron beams to support flat arches

The stone pier remaining from Woodlands footbridge can be spotted on the canal bank

A flat terrace above the canal that is now a garden was once the **wharf for Quinta colliery** and brickworks ❸. The business produced coal and bricks in the mid-nineteenth century, which were brought by a horse-operated tramroad for loading onto boats.

A small trade complex grew up where **Chirk Bank bridge 21** ❹ carried the Oswestry to Llangollen turnpike road over the new canal. The bridge had an innovative design of a very flat stone arch supported by curved cast-iron beams. This allowed traffic to cross without the steep approaches found at the typical hump-backed bridges. Goods were transhipped between road and canal at **public wharves** on both sides of the bridge. At one time a warehouse and stables also stood here. **Canal View Cottages** ❺ were built by the canal company for maintenance staff. One of them

was once a pub. About 100m beyond Chirk Bank bridge a stone pier on the opposite side of the canal from the towpath is the remains of a **footbridge** ❻. In the trees south of the canal was the **quarry** ❼ that produced the building stone for Chirk aqueduct.

Aqueduct Cottages ❽ at Chirk Bank were built in the late nineteenth century by the Shropshire Union Railways and Canal Company to house men working on the Glyn Valley tramway. They were made from the region's bright red brick and had a privy and pigsty block at the end of the gardens. A corrugated-iron **maintenance shed** ❾ in a yard between the cottages was built in the twentieth century for tools and materials to keep the canal in working order.

As the canal began its crossing of the Ceiriog valley, the huge **Chirk Bank terrace embankment** ❿ was needed – 0.7 miles

Some of the canal workers' houses at Aqueduct Cottages

'The most beautiful canal in the country.
It has simply everything…'
Frederic Doerflinger,
Slow Boat through England, 1970

long and made up of earth cut from the hillside above. The terrace was made especially wide where the cottages now stand to create a level **construction yard** ⑪ to prepare materials for Chirk aqueduct. Where it turns towards the valley the embankment is 18.3m high and 60m across at its base. A damaging breach happened here on 28 December 1816. As early as 1808, the canal company had feared subsidence from Chirk Bank colliery, which was below the canal, and they had asked

their engineer to survey the workings. When the embankment failed eight years later, water cascaded into the valley, destroying the mine and drowning the horses. Luckily, it was the only night for several years when no men were at work. Although the breach was almost certainly caused by the mine, a court case decided the canal company should pay damages.

The embankment leads straight onto the magnificent Chirk aqueduct ⑫, described in the next section.

The terrace embankment approaching Chirk aqueduct (on the left in this view) was made wide enough for a yard to prepare materials for building the aqueduct itself. It was used later for houses and gardens for canal workers

Chirk aqueduct and tunnel

Chirk tunnel and aqueduct are a few minutes' walk from either Chirk railway station or Chirk town centre. There is a car park near Chirk tunnel, at the Glyn Wylfa Centre and café on Castle Road (B4500). A short path leads down to the tunnel and aqueduct from the junction of Castle Road and Station Road.

This ten-arch aqueduct completed in 1801 was the tallest boat-carrying aqueduct in the world before Pontcysyllte. The engineers developed new methods to build a light and stable structure, leaving voids in the stonework and forming the canal bed with cast-iron plates. On the north side of the valley the canal went into a tunnel, which was one of the first in Britain to have a towpath. A wharf between the aqueduct and the tunnel served the town of Chirk.

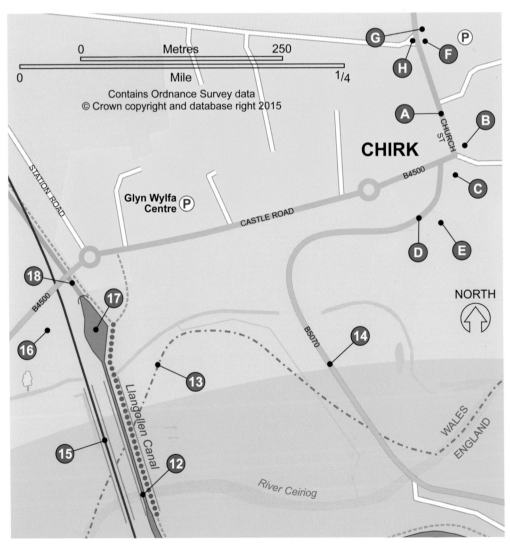

The central arches of Chirk aqueduct, with the later railway viaduct behind

Chirk aqueduct ⑫ appears at first sight like a conventional stone aqueduct, but it was far from conventional in design. Initially, Jessop and Telford planned to build a long embankment across the valley and an aqueduct over the river, but Sir Richard Myddleton of Chirk Castle objected that this would spoil views in his estate. The engineers then devised a detour up the valley to cross in a less visible location. But eventually they chose an aqueduct of unprecedented length and height that would stride across the valley and have almost no approach embankments – so that, as Jessop said, 'instead of an obstruction it would be a romantic feature in the view.'

Several stone and clay aqueducts on other canals had suffered from structural problems. This showed the engineers that a multi-span aqueduct of this height – 20.7m above the river Ceiriog – would need new techniques (page 40–3). They decided to build hollow stone arches on which iron plates rested to form the bed of the canal. The foundation stone was laid in June 1796 and the aqueduct opened five years later. The sides of the trough were waterproofed

originally with high-fired brick and hydraulic mortar and faced in stone but iron side plates were installed in 1869. Only the thickness of an iron plate separates the top of the arches from the bed of the waterway, greatly reducing the bulk and weight of the structure. The resulting elegant proportions, sweeping approaches and unembellished architecture embodied Telford's belief that beauty came from fitness for purpose.

As you cross the aqueduct you pass between England and Wales. The border cuts diagonally across the valley on the downstream side of the canal following the **old river course** ⑬, which can be made out as a low depression. The river was probably straightened by the engineers to avoid flood damage to the piers of the aqueduct.

If you look down the valley from the aqueduct you can see the wooded **Holyhead Road embankment** ⑭ rising to Chirk from a bridge over the Ceiriog. Telford was commissioned by Parliament in 1811 to improve the road connecting London to Dublin (see page 87). The embankment up to Chirk was a large engineering work, providing carriages with an even gradient of 1 in 20.

Chirk aqueduct in a watercolour by Sir Richard Colt Hoare on 6 June 1799 with six of the ten arches completed and a construction deck in use. He wrote 'stopped to take a view of the noble aqueduct that is forming across the valley'. The engineer's house, Telford Lodge, is in the distance

The elegant lines of Chirk aqueduct, with the railway viaduct beyond

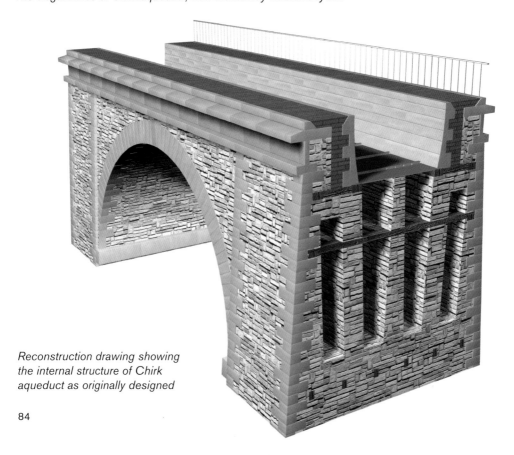

Reconstruction drawing showing the internal structure of Chirk aqueduct as originally designed

Chirk from the air in 1947. The railway viaduct and aqueduct are on the left. On the right below the town Telford's Holyhead Road embankment can be seen, before it was obscured by trees

Towering over the aqueduct is **Chirk viaduct** ⑮, built for the Shrewsbury and Chester Railway, which was to compete with the canal for traffic in the later nineteenth century. The viaduct was designed by Henry Robertson and built in 1846–8. Originally it had ten stone arches and timber side spans, but the timber was replaced with six additional stone spans in 1858. The highly-engineered route of the railway illustrates how the discoveries of the canal age were carried forward into later transport engineering. Beyond the viaduct on the north side of the valley stands **Telford Lodge** or Min-y-waen ⑯, a house probably built in about 1795 to accommodate a resident engineer and a drawing office for the engineering work on this stretch of the canal.

At the north end of the aqueduct a shelf was cut into the hillside and embanked outwards to make space for a canal basin and a **public wharf** ⑰. This was the

The basin and wharf between Chirk aqueduct and tunnel

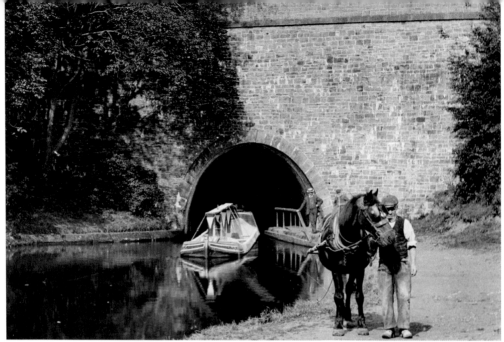

A fully laden narrow boat towed by a horse photographed in about 1910 emerging from Chirk tunnel

'It is the greatest Works, I believe, that is in hand in the kingdom and will not be completed for many years to come.' Thomas Telford, 1793

CHIRK AQUEDUCT.

terminus of the canal in 1801–2. The basin is a waiting point for the tunnel and the aqueduct, where boats cannot pass one another.

The work to build **Chirk tunnel** ⑱ took from 1795 to 1802. Earlier tunnels were narrower and boats had to be 'legged' slowly through by boatmen or labourers, but this tunnel had a towpath supported on brick arches with an iron handrail. The tunnel entrance flares slightly to make it easier for boats to enter and the railing curves into the ground so as not to snag the tow-rope. The high wall above the portal holds back the ground that was cut away.

Chirk aqueduct and tunnel, drawn by Percival Skelton before the railway viaduct was built: published in Samuel Smiles' The Lives of the Engineers

It is possible to walk through the tunnel, taking care in the dark of trip hazards and low headroom (a torch is helpful) – see page 89. Please do not cycle through the tunnel.

Telford's Holyhead Road

After completing the Ellesmere Canal, Telford oversaw the creation of the Holyhead Road, from London to Dublin via north Wales. The road runs roughly parallel with the canal from south of Chirk to Llantysilio – the whole length of the World Heritage site – and passes through Chirk and Llangollen. It was one of the great engineering achievements of the era and included major embankments, cuttings, causeways and bridges, including the iron Waterloo bridge at Betws-y-coed and the magnificent Menai suspension bridge across the Menai Strait to Anglesey, then the largest suspension bridge ever built.

Following the Act of Union between Britain and Ireland in 1801, travel between London and Dublin had to be improved, particularly for fast mail coaches. Telford was commissioned by the British parliament to make proposals for the improvement of the route in 1811. This included joining together existing roads but also building new sections, especially in north Wales. Telford applied lessons he had learned through his work on the canal, especially in engineering design and contract management.

Work began in 1815 and was completed in 1826 with the opening of the Menai bridge. As well as the great engineering works, many smaller features of the road can still be seen, including the carefully-graded formation, square alcoves in roadside walls for storing road-mending materials, milestones with cast-iron plates and houses for the toll-keepers. Telford also made significant improvements to the harbour at Holyhead. The road greatly reduced travel times from London to Dublin and was heavily used until railways took over passenger traffic after 1850.

An engraving of Telford's Menai suspension bridge taking the Holyhead Road to Anglesey, after a drawing by Henry Gastineau, 1830

Chirk and Chirk Castle

Chirk Castle sits on high ground a mile north-west of the aqueduct, looking out across the Dee valley. Although it was built as a thirteenth-century fortress it became a great country house under the Myddleton family, who owned mines and ironworks locally. Sir Richard Myddleton MP was a leading shareholder in the canal, and the engineers designed Chirk aqueduct and the tunnels and cuttings to its north so as to preserve the approaches to his landscaped park (pages 81 and 90). Chirk Castle is now owned by the National Trust.

The Hand Hotel in Chirk was an important stop on the journey to Holyhead

The town of Chirk – Y Waun in Welsh – is a five-minute walk from Chirk canal basin eastwards along Castle Road – see map on page 80. It began as a planned medieval borough but the canal helped it to grow as a coal-mining village. When Thomas Telford's Holyhead Road threaded through the town from south to north in the nineteenth century it brought new trade **A**. The medieval St Mary's church **B** where Castle Road and Church Street meet has monuments to the Myddletons. Across Trevor Road is a fine eighteenth-century house, The Mount, behind which the defensive 'motte' or castle mound recorded in 1165 is visible over the garden wall **C**. Telford's road climbs on a steady gradient **D** (page 85) but from the footpath in the field below the motte you can see the scars left from the ever-changing dog-legs by which the old road climbed the hill **E** before Telford's improvements.

Returning north on Church Street – the Holyhead Road – the three-storey Hand Hotel **F** served the London-Dublin traffic as well as local needs. Beyond this are two Victorian school buildings **G** (one for boys and one for girls) separated by Chirk estate cottages built in a gothic style in the 1820s. The war memorial **H** is by the sculptor and typeface designer Eric Gill.

Chirk Castle

Chirk tunnel to Irish Bridge 3

2.2 miles of level towpath. It is possible to walk through the tunnels, taking care in the dark of trip hazards and low headroom (a torch is helpful). Please do not cycle through the tunnels. There is a car park at the Glyn Wylfa Centre and café on Castle Road (B4500) in Chirk. A path goes down to the tunnel entrance from the junction of Castle Road and Station Road. There is limited space to park beside the canal at Irish bridge, off the B5605.

From Chirk the canal passes through two tunnels and two deep cuttings. These expensive engineering works made a direct route despite the higher ground, avoiding a long detour east. They also hid the canal from the approaches to Chirk Castle park.

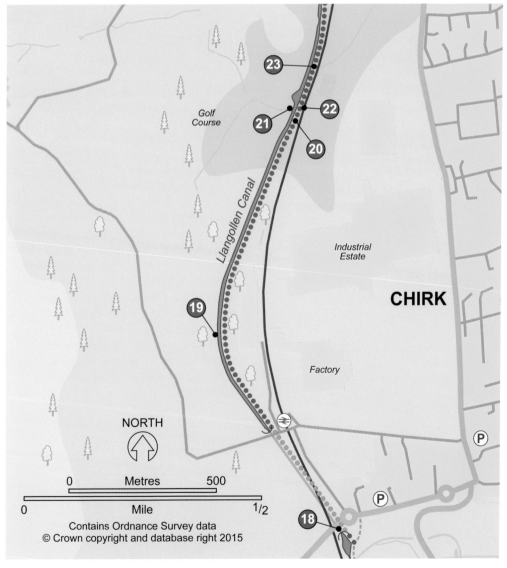

Golf Course

Llangollen Canal

Industrial Estate

CHIRK

Factory

NORTH

0   Metres   500

0   Mile   1/2

Contains Ordnance Survey data
© Crown copyright and database right 2015

The tunnels and cuttings on this section of the canal were major engineering works for their day

Chirk tunnel ⑱ is the longest on the Ellesmere canal, at 420m. (For the entrance see page 86.) A blocked shaft in the tunnel roof suggests that part may have been dug conventionally, but Telford largely used a cut-and-cover technique described in 1801: 'the ground, though deep, was cut open in different lengths, which afforded an opportunity of making brickwork very perfect, and securing the top of the arch with clay and loose stones, to prevent the waters of the upper strata from injuring the work.'

The canal emerges into **Canal Wood cutting** ⑲, which continues for three-quarters of a mile. A vast volume of material

had to be excavated here by navvies working with picks and shovels and animal-powered barrow inclines. The sides were gently graded and planted with trees to avoid the risk of slumping. The towpath and canal were kept at full width so boats could pass one another easily, even though this greatly increased the amount of material to be dug and moved. Most of the spoil was carried to build embankments further down the route, but the excess was dumped above the cutting at a safe distance from the edge (see drawing). Walking through Canal Wood Cutting in 1819 the young scientist Michael Faraday noted 'the sides were thickly planted with trees forming a very handsome grove'.

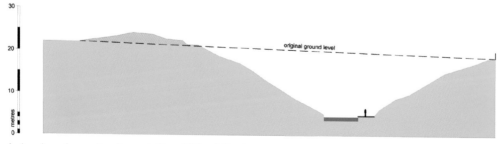

A drawing of a section through Canal Wood Cutting

Navvies using horse-powered barrow inclines at Tring railway cutting, by J. C. Bourne 1837

Near the north end of the cutting a wall beside the towpath marks a wharf for the **Glyn Valley tramway** ⓴. This narrow-gauge railway had been built in 1873 to connect slate quarries in Glyn Ceiriog to the canal at Gledrid. Wagons ran down part of the 6-mile route by gravity and were pulled on the rest by horses. In 1888, steam locomotives were introduced, and the line was rerouted

to meet the canal here and the Great Western Railway at Chirk Station.

On the opposite bank a watercourse enters the canal – the **Afon Bradley feeder** ㉑. Until the Llangollen feeder branch was completed in 1808 there was no reliable water supply for the canal, so the engineers collected from streams wherever they could. This was one of the largest.

This wall marks where the Glyn Valley tramway came to the canal in 1888

The towpath continues inside the tunnels

A turning basin marks where Thomas Ward brought his tramroad from Black Park colliery in 1805 and created a private **loading dock** ㉒ in a spur east of the canal. In the 1950s the dock was filled in but its bricked-up entrance can be made out in the edge of the towpath. A photograph of a narrowboat here in 1910 shows the small bridge that carried the towpath over the spur (page 66).

The turning basin opposite the entrance to the filled-in Black Park colliery loading dock

Roughly 100m beyond the basin is one of the features built on the canal to manage the water and avoid flooding – **the Bradley overflow** ㉓. It consists of a carefully-built overflow weir to draw off excess water, a culvert to take it away under the embankment and sluice gear to lower the level or drain the canal for repairs.

The canal next enters the shallow **Red Bridge cutting** ㉔. At the end of this a group

of small **limekilns** ㉕ stood beside the towpath. Some overgrown remains of the kilns can be seen in winter, built of rubble with brick arches. They probably produced mortar to build the canal's structures and then later produced quicklime for sale down the finished waterway.

The ruins of the Afon Bradley limekilns. The arches for drawing out the burnt lime at the bottom of the kiln can be seen

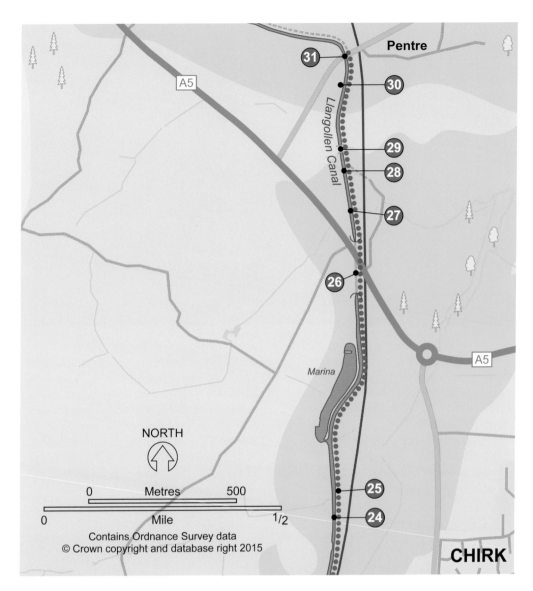

Whitehouses tunnel

Both tunnels have towpaths and are lined in brick

After passing Chirk marina, a recent addition to one side of the canal, a cutting leads to **Whitehouses tunnel** ㉖, another shallow cut-and-cover tunnel with a towpath. The canal keeps its nearly straight line over **small embankments** at Pen-y-bryn ㉗ and Pentre ㉘, each with a stream culvert beneath it. **Whitehouse bridge 26** ㉙ marks the entrance to **Irish Bridge cutting** ㉚. This 370m-long cutting is up to 10m deep and

one of the most impressive on the canal. The large amounts of spoil excavated from it were all transported on construction railways to the great approach embankment for Pontcysyllte aqueduct a mile away. **Irish Bridge 27** itself ㉛ is based on the standard bridge design for the canal but amended to fit the cutting with an exceptionally high arch and level approaches.

Irish Bridge is similar to others on the canal but much taller to carry a road at a level across a cutting

Irish Bridge to Pontcysyllte aqueduct embankment

1.4 miles of level towpath. There is limited space to park beside the canal at Irish Bridge, off the B5605. There is a car park next to the canal basin at Froncysyllte.

After Irish Bridge the canal is terraced for a mile along the steep side of the Dee valley at Froncysyllte, where a wharf and basin served limestone quarries and kilns. The canal then pushes out across the valley on a massive embankment to approach Pontcysyllte aqueduct.

Irish Bridge cutting ㉛ ends near the bridge and the canal turns from north to west to follow the Dee valley. Just beyond the bend, a flat area next to the towpath was a **wharf** ㉜ for limestone and quicklime brought by a tramway from Froncysyllte and after about 1900 for bricks and tiles brought by a mineral railway from Pen-y-bont brick and tile works down in the valley to the north. The works was owned by J. C. Edwards and made bricks, tiles and decorative terracotta from local clay that produced a distinctive bright red colour when it was fired. Even in 1900, the canal still provided a cheap alternative to rail transport.

A **terrace embankment** ㉝ carries the canal along the steep slope and crosses the ancient Offa's Dyke ㉞. A **shallow cutting** ㉟ breaks through a small bluff before a long

terraced section begins, still high above the valley. The risk of a sudden breach in the bank of the canal anywhere along this part of the route led the engineers to put frequent places for stop-planks. There are occasional views to the great **Cefn railway viaduct** ㊱, built in 1848 to carry the Shrewsbury and Chester Railway across the Dee valley.

Cross Street aqueduct ㊲ is visible from the canal as a narrower channel with stop-plank slots and a stone parapet on the towpath side. You can see the single arch under the canal if you go down the side of the embankment. This was a small structure compared with Chirk and Pontcysyllte aqueducts, so it was possible to build it traditionally with stone walling and puddled clay. It is easy to see why such bulky

The one-arch Cross Street aqueduct, built by conventional methods with stone walls waterproofed with thick layers of clay

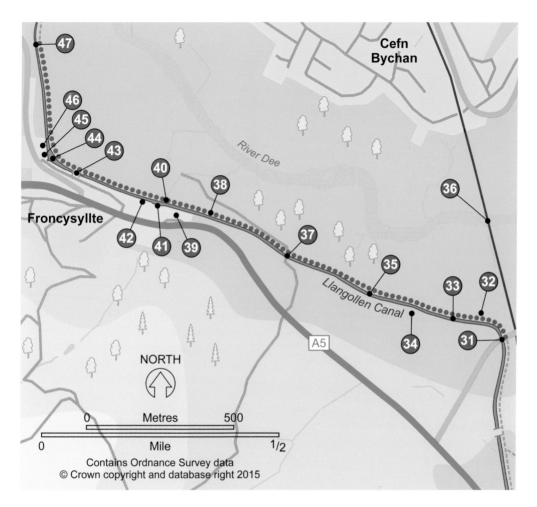

construction would have been too expensive and too unstable for multiple spans at great heights. The aqueduct brought a track under the canal where the lie of the land did not allow for the more normal over-bridge. Later it was used by a railway from limekilns at Froncysyllte to the main-line railway at Irish Bridge. Remains can be seen of turntables that turned wagons around the tight corners on each side.

After Cross Street aqueduct, the canal is terraced in **Fron embankment** ㊳. A series of wharves on the south side of the canal starts as you come to Froncysyllte. The huge stone wall rising above the canal is **Froncysyllte east limekilns** ㊴. These were

begun before 1820 to make quicklime by burning limestone with coal brought by canal. The limestone came on a horse-worked tramroad and a series of inclines from the Pen-y-graig quarries, a mile away above the canal in Froncysyllte. The tramroad came down to the wharves through a tunnel under the Holyhead Road, which passed behind the kilns. Another group of kilns was built above the road.

Just beyond the first group of kilns is a **sluice** ㊵ for draining the canal into a culvert beneath the embankment. There was once a **loading dock** ㊶ on the south side of the canal, created in an indent in the hillside where a stream entered the canal. The dock

An aerial view of the Dee valley approaching the crossing at Pontcysyllte. The canal occupies a terrace on the near side of the valley to Froncysyllte then strikes out across the great wooded embankment to the aqueduct. In the foreground is Telford's Holyhead Road, now the A5

is now buried but it was used to offload coal and collect quicklime. **Froncysyllte west limekilns** ㊷ are two smaller banks of early-nineteenth-century limekilns on their own wharf. Originally owned by the ironmaster William Hazledine, these were connected to a different limestone quarry in Froncysyllte by a horse-worked tramroad. Pisgah quarry can be visited as it is now a wooded nature reserve maintained by North Wales Wildlife Trust with trails around the old workings.

Fron footbridge and lift bridge 28 ㊸ mark the arrival at Froncysyllte basin. The lifting bridge is similar to those built on the canal in places where it was not convenient to cross the canal on a hump-backed bridge, for example because of lack of space. The original timber bridge was opened by pulling a rope to lift the deck. The present steel bridge uses hydraulics but is otherwise of a similar design. The footbridge was added in the mid-twentieth century so that people could cross the canal when the lift bridge was open.

The **public wharf** ㊹ at Froncysyllte was the terminus of the canal from 1802 until Pontcysyllte aqueduct was completed in 1805. Boats could turn in the large basin by

Froncysyllte institute and the workers' mess beyond

putting their prow into the corner while the stern was pulled around with a rope. The wharf continued to be used for general trade. The red brick **house** ㊺ on the north side of the basin was built in the late nineteenth century by the Shropshire Union Railways and Canal Company to house an employee and his family. The company also provided **Froncysyllte mess and institute** ㊻, the small stone building next to the towpath as the canal turns north out of the basin, as a mess for maintenance workers and a workers' institute offering some education for boat children.

The largest of the great banks of limekilns standing above the canal at Froncysyllte. The archways for drawing out the burnt lime at the bottom can still be made out.

Fron lift bridge in its original timber form in 1936

Drawing of a section through the approach embankment to Pontcysyllte aqueduct

After turning north the canal heads straight out across the valley towards Pontcysyllte aqueduct. The great earth **approach embankment** ㊼ was built between 1795 and 1805 to designs by Telford and Jessop and the contractor William Davies. The embankment is 610m long and reaches a height of 23m at its far end. It was built with spoil brought from the cuttings between here and Chirk on three temporary railways – a prime example of the canal's pioneering uses of railways for construction purposes. It is hard now to appreciate the scale of the embankment owing to the trees planted to stabilise it. At the time of its completion, it was one of the largest civil earthworks ever built.

How Pontcysyllte aqueduct was built

The sandstone for the 18 piers of Pontcysyllte aqueduct was quarried on the nearby ridge at Cefn Mawr. It was brought – almost certainly by a horse-worked tramroad – to the construction yard for the aqueduct, sited where Trevor basin is now. It was cut into blocks and dressed by masons and then probably lowered to the level where it was required by a counterbalanced tramroad incline. Some drawings of the time and the evidence of the stonework itself show that the piers were built up a stage at a time and supported temporary timber bridges that carried the construction tramroad. The masons built up to the next level of each pier, starting at the furthest and working back towards the Trevor end. The temporary bridges were then dismantled and moved up to the new level until the piers were all at full height. The piers were hollow in their upper parts to make them lighter.

The engineers paid unusual attention to the safety of the workforce. Jessop wrote to Telford in 1795, 'In looking forward to the time when we shall be laying the Iron Trough on the Piers I foresee some difficulties that appear to me formidable – In the first place I see the men giddy and terrified in laying stones with such an immense depth underneath them with only a space of 6 feet wide and 10 feet long to stand upon'. He recommended that the piers be widened. Telford wrote years later in his autobiography, 'one man only fell during the whole of the operations in building the piers, and affixing the iron work upon their summit, and this took place from carelessness on his part'.

The ribs for the arches and the plates for the trough were all cast at William Hazledine's Plas Kynaston iron foundry, which he established for the purpose half a mile to the north. The parts were brought together in the construction yard and numbered so that they could be put together in the correct order. The arched ribs were put up first, then the trough was bolted over them and the towpath and handrail were added.

The aqueduct trough from the side, showing the plates bolted together and the thin iron ribs that support it

Telford's 1822 portrait by Samuel Lane hangs in the
Institution of Civil Engineers. Over his shoulder it shows
Pontcysyllte aqueduct. In time it began to be forgotten that
Jessop was its joint designer.

A painting dated 1805 by Moses Griffith in the National Museum of Wales shows Pontcysyllte aqueduct during construction. Some of the temporary wooden access bridges and two cranes are still in place

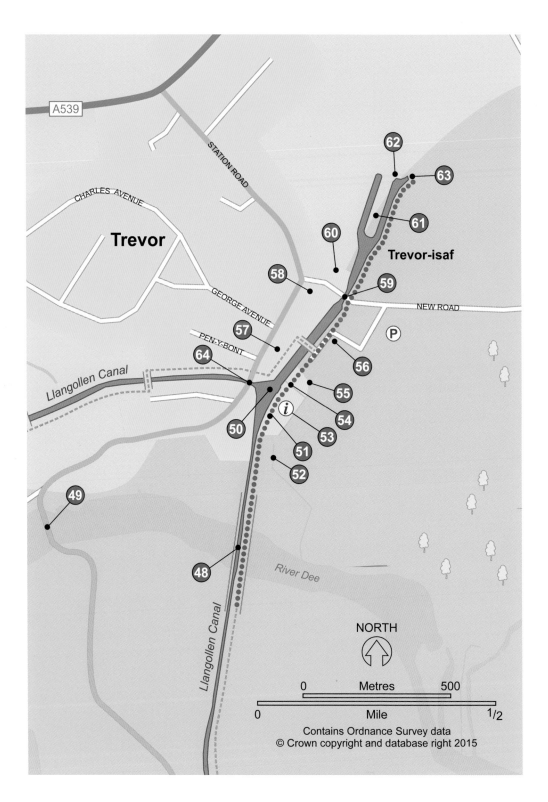

Right: A drawing of Pontcysyllte aqueduct by George Yates in the year it was completed, issued as a Romantic print

Pontcysyllte aqueduct and Trevor basin

Pontcysyllte aqueduct is signposted from the A539 Llangollen-Ruabon road. At Trevor turn down Station Road and New Road and follow signs to the aqueduct car parks. Walk on the level towpath for 200m to the aqueduct. Safety note: the towpath over the aqueduct is narrow and you must take care passing people. Cycling is not permitted. Children must be supervised closely and please note that the original railings are sufficiently widely spaced for a toddler to squeeze between them.

Begun in 1795, the monumental Pontcysyllte aqueduct is the centrepiece of the World Heritage site. Jessop and Telford's application of the new technology of cast iron to create the tallest and longest navigable aqueduct in the world was a daring achievement. The 'waterway through the sky' was opened on 26 November 1805 with a procession of boats, music, gunfire and cheers from 8,000 spectators. The site of the aqueduct construction yard became a busy trading basin.

Pontcysyllte aqueduct 48 is known internationally as a masterpiece of engineering. Standing next to it and looking across the valley it is easy to see why. It seems so light and delicate, and yet its dimensions are staggering. Eighteen tapering stone piers carry a narrow trough of iron plates for a distance of 307m. There is only 25mm between the water inside and the thin air. It is 38.4m from the water level of the canal to the river below. Pontcysyllte remained the tallest navigable aqueduct in the world for 200 years (it was superseded only in the twenty-first century by aqueducts

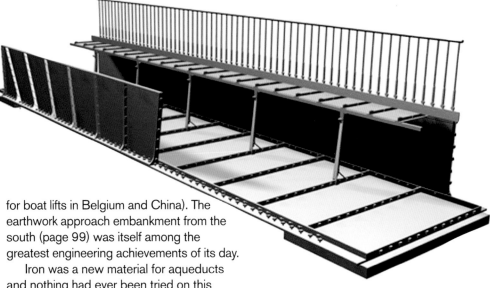

for boat lifts in Belgium and China). The earthwork approach embankment from the south (page 99) was itself among the greatest engineering achievements of its day.

Iron was a new material for aqueducts and nothing had ever been tried on this scale. The evolution of the design is described on page 40–3, and a feature on page 100 explains how it was built. Walking across you can see how the great **cast-iron plates** fit together. They were fixed with bolts through flanges on the outer surfaces of the side plates and the upward-facing surfaces of the bed plates (what you see at the edge of the trough is the fixing flange, not the much thinner profile of the plate). The joints were filled with Welsh flannel, white lead and iron borings to make them watertight.

The **towpath** extends out over the channel supported by vertical posts (originally timber but replaced with iron in the nineteenth century). This design feature meant both that the forces on the piers were balanced from side to side and that water could flow past loaded boats even though they sat deep in the channel. The walkway is made of dished iron plates over which the surface material is laid. The cast-iron **handrail** uprights are fixed into lug-holes on the trough plates. No railing was ever intended on the other side of the canal –

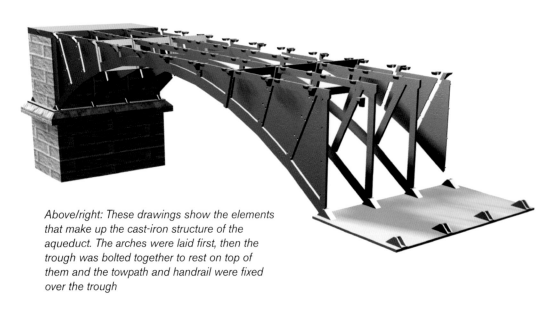

Above/right: These drawings show the elements that make up the cast-iron structure of the aqueduct. The arches were laid first, then the trough was bolted together to rest on top of them and the towpath and handrail were fixed over the trough

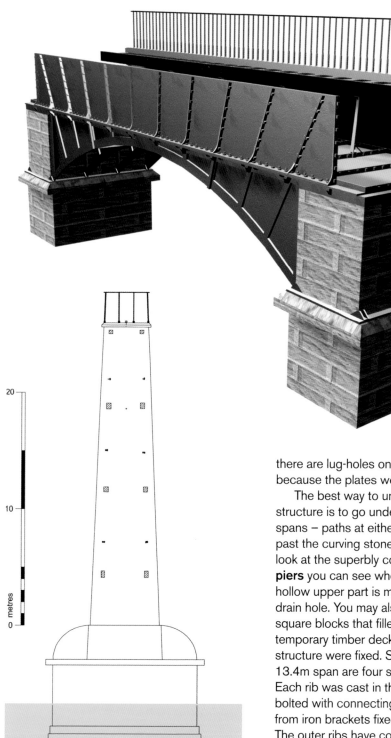

A drawing of a pier showing the marks that can still be seen to indicate where the temporary construction bridges were fixed

there are lug-holes on that side only because the plates were identical.

The best way to understand the structure is to go underneath one of the spans – paths at either end lead down past the curving stone **abutments**. If you look at the superbly constructed **stone piers** you can see where the start of the hollow upper part is marked by a circular drain hole. You may also be able make out square blocks that filled where the temporary timber decks used to build the structure were fixed. Supporting each 13.4m span are four slender **iron ribs**. Each rib was cast in three sections and bolted with connecting plates. They rise from iron brackets fixed in the stonework. The outer ribs have cover plates to make them *appear* more solid. The **trough** is 3.61m wide and rests on top of the ribs but is not fixed to them, just prevented by lugs and by its own weight from sideways movement. The side plates of the trough lock together in a pattern similar to the stones in a flat arch. On the outside surfaces you can see the nuts and bolts that hold the plates together through the flanges.

On the river Dee below is **Pont Cysylltau** 49 – a three-arch stone bridge from which the aqueduct took its name. It was built almost exactly a century before the canal, in 1697. It carries a minor road and provides a fine view of the aqueduct.

Trevor basin 50 was built on a terrace retained by a stone wall. This was created originally as the construction yard for the aqueduct. It then became the terminal basin of the main line and the junction point for the Llangollen branch (page 119) through the bridge to the west 64. Just

A stone channel takes waste water from the canal down the hill to the river Dee

north of the aqueduct an **overflow** 51 takes water by a culvert under the towpath and the platform area next to it to a stone **channel** 52 that took water safely down to

Trevor basin from the air. On the right the canal widens from the aqueduct to the junction with the Llangollen branch, opposite the dry docks and interpretation centre. The main line ended on the left, in the 'tuning-fork' shaped arms where it met tramroads and the Plas Kynaston canal

the river, avoiding any risk of damaging the aqueduct piers. The brick **workshops and stores** ➌ of the late nineteenth century are now the World Heritage site interpretation centre. A hearth behind was for boiling pitch to waterproof and preserve timber and iron.

A **swing footbridge** ➍ crosses the entrances to a pair of **dry docks** where for two hundred years boats have been brought for repair work. Gates close off the canal so that the water can be drained away. The docks are rare survivors of hundreds that existed on British canals. They were built by Telford in about 1806, though the cover building was added in the twentieth century. The swing bridge probably also dates originally from 1806 and is similar to swivel bridges on Telford and Jessop's later

Caledonian Canal. Beyond this is a **dock manager's house** ➎ that was built in the mid-nineteenth century and later used as a pub. A corrugated iron **shed** ➏ stored maintenance equipment.

A swing bridge carries the towpath over the entrance to a dry dock

The dock manager's house. The gable shows that the roof was raised

Each side of the canal was once filled with horse-operated rail lines bringing coal, iron and other goods to the head of the canal. A small stone-built **warehouse** ⑤⑦ on the west side would have been used for general goods that needed protection from the weather. In an imposing position looking back towards the aqueduct is **Scotch Hall** or the **Telford Inn** ⑤⑧, which was built before 1803 for the supervising engineer, Matthew Davidson. Telford would have stayed here during his visits. The proportions and hipped slate roof with overhanging eaves are typical of Telford's work as an architect. The single-storey building by the bridge is believed to have been the **accounts house** for the construction project.

Scotch Hall Bridge 29 ⑤⑨ is one of Telford's innovative bridges with a flattened stone arch supported by curved cast iron beams so as to provide gently

The account house next to Scotch Hall

A former warehouse at the basin

Scotch Hall or the Telford Inn

The stone-built loading pier that divides the canal into two arms at its terminus

graded approaches for road traffic (page 33 and 36). Two side-arches were added to allow railway lines to pass under the road. A short walk under the bridge leads to the very end of the main-line canal. Just behind the bridge is a **wharfinger's house** ⑳, which was built possibly as early as 1805 as accommodation for an overseer

The entrance to the former Plas Kynaston canal

of the wharf. The canal splits either side of a long **stone pier** ㊶ which carried three more lines of rail tracks for loading boats on either side. It was built between 1803 and 1805 to a design by Telford and Thomas Denson. They also designed the horse-operated Ruabon Brook railway to serve industries to the north (page 46).

At the end of the eastern spur is a **loading dock** ㊷ wide enough for one boat. This was once covered over by a warehouse for goods to be transferred between horse-drawn railway wagons and narrowboats. The blocked **stone arch** ㊸ to its right was the entrance to the short Plas Kynaston branch canal – see page 58–9. The branch was filled in during the 1950s but there are hopes that it might one day be reopened.

Trevor basin in around 1840

Rose Cottage, pictured in the 1940s, was originally a canal company office and later a wharf-keeper's house

Warehouse and crane at Llangollen

This drawing suggests how the head of the main line at Trevor might have looked in 1840. The two basins are busy with boats taking away coal, bricks and iron products and bringing in limestone and general trade. Roads and horse-worked tramroads connect the canal to the surrounding area. Buildings around the wharves include the boatyard opposite the junction with the Llangollen branch, a warehouse, houses for canal workers and Scotch Hall. The pier on the right extends the space for loading, as does a narrow loading dock next to it, the width of a single boat.

113

The head of the main line in around 1875

This drawing reconstructs the area at the head of the main line in
1875. Many railway sidings still connect with the canal but by this
time small locomotives as well as horses are drawing the trains of
wagons. A transhipment warehouse has been built over the
boat dock (top right) so that valuable goods can be
moved between the railway and the canal under cover.
On the far right is the entrance to the private
Plas Kynaston Canal (see page 58–9).

Horses and wagons – detail from photograph on page 123

115

Cefn Mawr

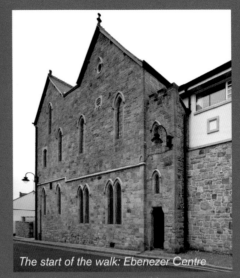

The start of the walk: Ebenezer Centre

While Chirk and Llangollen grew more prosperous as a result of the canal, Cefn Mawr was a new town created by the opportunities the canal brought for industry. Little stood on the 'great ridge' (the literal translation of 'cefn mawr') before the nineteenth century, when a settlement grew up around stone quarries, ironworks, clay works and coal mines. The stone for Pontcysyllte aqueduct came from Cefn. An estate map of 1804 showed just Plas Kynaston house and a handful of farms and mines. By 1845, buildings lay strung out along lanes and the Ruabon Brook tramroad. Landowners did not attempt to plan the community, and houses were built by squatters. Cefn was described in 1838 as 'a large straggling village'.

A good place to begin a walk is Ebenezer **A** , a Baptist chapel of 1873 with a modern glass extension, now a community centre. Nonconformist religion was popular in industrial communities, and chapels were built by different denominations. Some fine commercial buildings sit on Well Street **B** . If you walk down Hill Street, the house with the tall red-brick chimneys below the road is Plas Kynaston **C** , where the industrialist Exuperius Pickering lived in the early nineteenth century. Steps lead down to its front.

Return to Crane Street and turn left passing the gothic side of the Ebenezer Centre. The narrow, curving, nearly level route of the street **D** is a clue to its origin as a tramroad that branched off the Ruabon Brook railway. This was colonised with shops, pubs and houses built of the local sandstone or later the red bricks made with local clay.

At the end of Crane Street, the Ruabon Brook tramroad came from Trevor basin up the lane to the right of the Post Office **E** . It turned back on itself through a hairpin

Plas Kynaston house in 1952

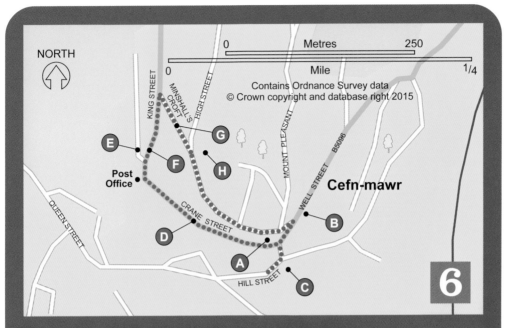

NORTH

Cefn-mawr

bend **F** up what was to become King Street. This corner is known as 'the Crane' and a crane here may have lifted goods on and off trucks. King Street has an even gradient for horse-hauled wagons. Take a narrow lane to the right, Minshall's Croft **G** . This may have been an incline from the sandstone quarries. Many buildings in the town are unusual shapes as they sit in plots left between railways and paths.

At the top of Minshalls Croft is High Street. You can turn right, back to the Ebenezer Centre, or go up the track nearly opposite **H** , where there are examples of stone tramroad sleepers. This leads across the ridge past some quarry sites.

Minshalls Croft may be an old incline from the quarries

One of the sandstone quarries on the great ridge, now occupied by a late nineteenth-century house

The beautiful scenery of the Dee valley, looking east from the air above the edge of Llangollen

Trevor basin to Llangollen

4.2 miles of level towpath. There is car parking at Trevor basin and in the town of Llangollen. The branch canal begins at Rhos-y-coed bridge 31. The towpath starts from Station Road on the north side of the canal.

The Llangollen branch of the canal stretches west from Trevor up the Dee valley, often high above the river and with panoramic views. It was built between 1804 and 1808 to designs by Telford and Thomas Denson to supply water to the main line and carry traffic. The standard width was smaller and the canal included many narrow sections owing to the steep slopes it had to negotiate.

Rhos-y-coed bridge is the entrance to the Llangollen branch

Rhos-y-coed bridge 31 ⑥④ is the first structure on the Llangollen branch. It was of the same innovative design as Scotch Hall bridge, with a flat arch and curved iron beams so as to carry road traffic (page 33 and 36). On the right-hand side of the road as it goes downhill towards Pont Cysylltau bridge (page 108), a high stone wall supported a level terrace that was part of the **construction yard** ⑥⑤ for Pontcysyllte aqueduct. The canal branch cut through the middle of the yard. Although the land is now mostly houses and gardens, in about 1823 Exuperius Pickering junior started an iron forge and coking ovens here. Lumps of iron slag can be seen in the woodland along the towpath.

The towpath begins on the north side of **Bont Wood cutting** ⑥⑥ and continues at a high level above the canal as far as **Postles bridge 32** ⑥⑦, where it crosses to the south. This is a change-over bridge, specially designed to carry the towpath over the

Postles bridge and its long ramp down to the towpath

119

Wood Bank is now a private house but it was once canal company offices and probably a drawing office for the design of the aqueduct

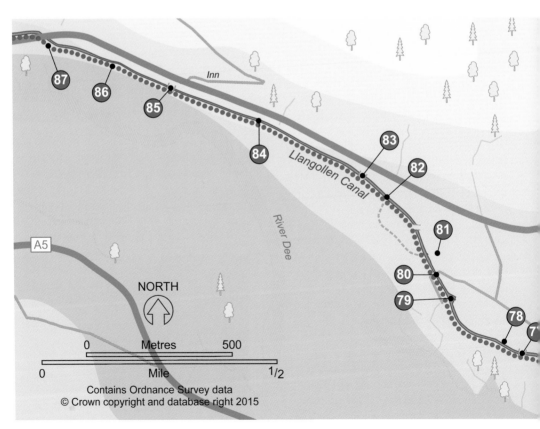

canal. It allowed the horse to cross the canal without obstructing its tow-rope. The ramp down points back towards Trevor so that the horse would take the rope underneath the bridge rather than over it. The stonework is original but the deck has been replaced.

As the canal enters the substantial **Wood Bank embankment** ⓺ you can see the back of a private house south of the canal called **Wood Bank** ⓺. This overlooks Pontcysyllte aqueduct and was probably the drawing office during its construction. The property was still owned by the canal company in 1838 and was described as 'house and offices, malt kiln and croft'. Some malt kilns survive at the rear. The large sash windows of the house would have given light for drawing and views across the whole length of the structure. Just beyond the house is **White footbridge**

33 ⓺, which has stone abutments and a steel deck that replaced the original timber.

Just after **Plas-yn-pentre bridge 34** ⓺ the canal comes to the large **Millars embankment** ⓺, below which Trevor corn mill (still with its large waterwheel) sits on a stream down to the river Dee. As the canal cut across the steep slopes towards Llangollen, the engineers had little room to vary their route. The mill pond was exactly where they wanted to build the embankment so Telford and Denson built a new mill pond above the canal and a culvert to bring the water safely beneath the embankment. Just before the next bridge a **wharf** ⓺ with a crane and store once served the corn mill and the adjacent road. **Millars Bridge 35** ⓺ is an example of the modification of the standard bridge design with an unusually wide arch to improve visibility and manoeuvrability on a bend.

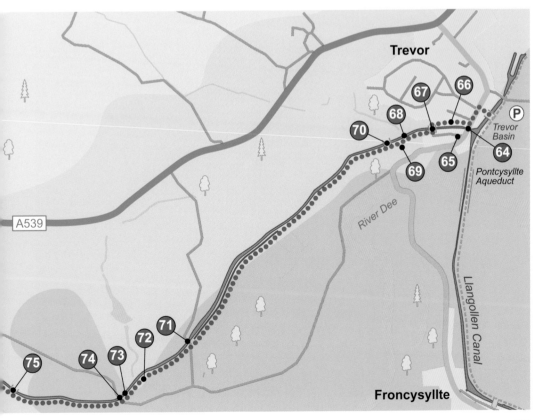

Bryn-Howel bridge

Bryn-ceirch bridge 36 ⑦ and **Plas-isaf bridge 37** ⑦ illustrate variations in the standard bridge design to allow for the slope. Between them, **Bryn-ceirch cutting** ⑦ is a cutting on one side and an embankment on the other. Part of the cutting was a gravel pit that probably provided materials for the canal. Just beyond Plas-isaf bridge there were two **wharves** ⑦ on the uphill side of the canal for limestone brought

by a tramroad and incline from Trevor Hall Wood quarry on the hill above, which was operated from the early nineteenth century by Exuperius Pickering junior. A bank of limekilns stood near the wharf where lime was burnt with coal brought by canal. About 100m further on, a **basin** ⑦ for boats to turn after using the wharves was made by the engineers by taking advantage of an indent in the hillside.

Bryn-Howel cutting leads to **Bryn-Howel bridge 38** ⑧, which is one of the most picturesque on the canal. Beyond it, a boat house in the garden of the adjacent mansion, now the **Bryn-Howel hotel** ⑧, shows that pleasure boating was becoming popular on the Llangollen branch at the end of the nineteenth century. A boat was kept here by James Coster Edwards, the owner of the great brick, tile and terracotta works in Cefn Mawr and Newbridge (page 61). The mansion and boat house were built in 1896 in 'Jacobethan' style using J. C. Edwards' products.

J. C. Edwards' pretty boat house at Bryn-Howel

A rare photograph of a working limestone wharf shows two narrow boats at Sun Trevor bridge, with its extra arch for the tramroad. One tram is drawn by a donkey and others lie near the tipping staithe. See details on pages 58 and 115

After the concrete railway bridge there was another **wharf** ⑧ for Trevor Hall Wood limestone quarries, which superseded the ones at Plas-isaf. An incline went directly up the hill to the quarries, now visible as a wooded cutting through the fields above the canal. A short terrace embankment leads to **Plas-ifan bridge 40** ⑧, where the engineers diverted the road slightly to ease the gradients up and over the bridge. A roofed shelter next to the bridge stores stop-planks ready to drop into the slots under the bridge in case of a sudden breach in the embankments. There were more **wharves** ⑧ for limestone quarries in the stretch leading up to **Sun Trevor bridge 41** ⑧, which has a small second arch for a tramroad from the quarries. Another incline came down from the quarries here: its line can be seen across the main road from the canal.

A ruined bridge crosses the incline from Sun Trevor wharf to the limestone quarries on the hill above, photographed in 1985

Sun Trevor bridge had arches for the canal and a quarry tramroad to serve a wharf alongside it

Llanddyn Cottage and adjacent bridge

Llanddyn lift bridge in 1936

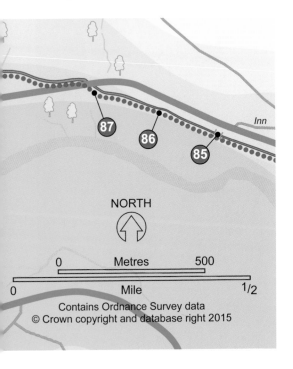

Contains Ordnance Survey data
© Crown copyright and database right 2015

The large **Sun Trevor terrace embankment** 86 was the site of a major breach in 1945 in which one person was killed (page 126). Just before the modern concrete road bridge at Wenffrwd a cast-iron **sluice paddle** 87 allows the canal to be drained for maintenance.

The red-brick **Llanddyn Cottage** 88 was built in the late nineteenth century by the Shropshire Union Railway and Canal Company as a lengthsman's house. **Llanddyn bridge 43** 89, beyond it, has stop planks to deal with any breach on the steep slopes. **Llanddyn lift bridge 44** 90 is a late twentieth-century bridge following the traditional lift-bridge form but operated hydraulically.

After the lift bridge the canal curves around an exceptionally steep, rocky slope, high above the main road, the old railway line and the river Dee. To traverse it the

Canal breaches and protection

The steep slopes the canal ran across meant that it was particularly at risk of breaches, sudden breaks in the canal banks. Among major breaches were those that flooded a colliery at Chirk Bank in 1816 (page 78), and three at different points near Bryn-Howel. The most disastrous was on the Sun Trevor terrace embankment on 7 September 1945. The force of the water moved thousands of tons of earth, creating a breach over 35m long and more than 15m deep and washing through the railway embankment further down the hill. An early morning goods train crashed, killing one person and injuring two engine crew. This showed the urgent need for bank protection and lining at vulnerable sections.

Early forms of bank protection included timber stakes, planks and brickwork. From the 1960s these were replaced with concrete edging or steel sheets. More recently, timbers held by steel beams or geotextile barriers have been preferred and repairs to quay walls have been done in stone. The earliest system of lining to replace the original puddled clay was asphalt, which was laid in the last part of the feeder channel above Pentrefelin in the 1950s. Concrete lining, applied in the 1980s, prevented leakage and created a strong, stable structure. The preferred method today is a plastic membrane with a concrete wall on the downhill side.

A photograph of one of the huge breaches in the canal at Bryn-Howel

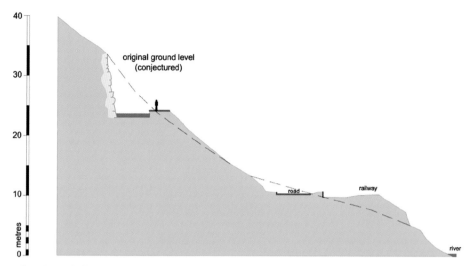

A section through the rock cuttings at Wern-isaf

engineers devised the dramatic **Wern-isaf rock cutting** ⑨ which has a vertical face into the hillside and an embankment opposite. They made the canal as narrow as possible, without room for boats to pass one another, and included frequent stop-plank grooves in case of breaches.

As the canal begins to enter Llangollen, a cluster of tall stone building below it is **Upper Dee Flannel Mills** ⑨, a woollen factory that operated from the mid-nineteenth century using water from the canal to power it. The water intake under the towpath can still be seen. This was the largest of several woollen mills that grew up in Llangollen after the canal was built. **Wharf Cottage** ⑨ is a wharfinger's cottage built into the retaining wall of the canal because of the difficult terrain.

Siambr-wen bridge 45 ⑨ is a twentieth-century structure but it is built on the abutments of an original over-bridge that was probably of Telford's composite design, as the cut-off ends of cast-iron beams can still be seen. Immediately after the bridge is **Llangollen Wharf** ⑨ (see page 131), from which the road leads down into Llangollen (page 128).

The picturesque Wern-isaf rock cutting

Llangollen

The town of Llangollen, which the canal branch served, is a short walk downhill from Llangollen wharf 95. It grew up in the Middle Ages at the site of a bridge over the river Dee. The town developed its textile industry in the early nineteenth century and it became a service centre after Telford's Holyhead Road (page 87) came through in the 1820s. Since 1947 it has been home to the International Musical Eisteddfod, which brings performers from all over the world, many of whom take boat trips on the canal: the poet Dylan Thomas wrote in 1953 that it 'spills colourfully, multilingually and confraternally into the streets of Llangollen and the surrounding countryside'.

At the heart of the town the stone bridge striding across the river A is an impressive example of the achievements of Jessop and Telford's medieval predecessors. It was rebuilt in about 1500, a span was added for the railway in the 1860s and it was widened upstream in the 1960s. The way through the town was originally Bridge Street B, which curves to the east towards the church, but Castle Street C was cut through from the bridge to the new Holyhead Road D in the mid-nineteenth century.

From the late eighteenth century, visitors were encouraged into the area by artists and writers who toured north Wales, often exploring the canal among other things. Many came to visit Plas Newydd E, the home between 1780 and 1829 of Lady Eleanor Butler and Miss Sara Ponsonby, the famous 'Ladies of Llangollen', who lived together there for over fifty years. Hotels and shops, the town museum F, the steam railway G and horse-drawn canal trips continue to serve visitors.

Visitors to the International Eisteddfod from many countries take a boat trip on the canal in 1960

8

NORTH

95

A542

G

Llangollen Canal

WERN ROAD

MILL STREET

A

Llangollen Bridge

F

Weir

B

Weir

A539

CASTLE STREET

BRIDGE STREET

River Dee

C

MARKET STREET

OAK STREET

CHURCH STREET

P

LLANGOLLEN

A5

BERWYN STREET

REGENT STREET

A5

D

BUTLERS HILL

| 0 | Metres | 250 |

| 0 | Mile | 1/4 |

E

Contains Ordnance Survey data
© Crown copyright and database right 2015

A drawing of the picturesque town of Llangollen and its bridge shortly before the canal arrived, in about 1780

The beautiful crescent weir at Horseshoe Falls is where the water for the canal is drawn from the river Dee

Llangollen wharf to Horseshoe Falls

9

1.8 miles of level towpath. The final part of the water feeder beyond Llangollen marina is not open to powered boats. There is car parking in Llangollen town and near Horseshoe Falls on the B5103.

The canal is at its narrowest beyond Llangollen. Boats traded in limestone, coal, slate and other goods as far as Chain Bridge. Beyond this a narrow feeder channel went on to the Dee at Horseshoe Falls, where Telford designed an elegant curving weir to draw water into the canal. Substantial engineering work was required to cut a shelf for the waterway in a constricted gorge. The rocky, wooded riverside has been a popular place to visit since the late nineteenth century.

When the canal branch was built Llangollen was already an important market town that needed coal and general goods and a minor centre of cotton and woollen manufacturing. The town was served by a public **wharf** 95 and a **warehouse**, which was built from local stone and extended in brick as trade grew. The warehouse is now a café and horse-drawn boat tours run from the wharf, as they have since 1884. Beyond the wharf is Llangollen **winding hole** 96, which was built as part of the original canal scheme. It allowed boats to turn as few would be going further. The winding hole is now part of a mooring basin enlarged in 2005. Powered boats are not allowed beyond this point.

Pen-y-ddol hill-slope **cutting** 97 and **Pen-y-ddol bridge 46** 98 lead to **Tower Bridge cutting** 99, a substantial terrace made by cutting into the hill-slope on one side and building an embankment on the other.

About 200m after **Pentrefelin bridge 48** 100 a narrowing in the canal shows where a **lift-bridge** 101 crossed to **Pentrefelin slate mill** 102, where slate was cut into slabs for architectural use. The mill now houses a motor museum. Slate was brought from quarries to the north in the Horseshoe Pass by the Oernant tramway, which was designed by the Cornish engineer Henry Dennis and opened in 1857. The tramway went 4.5 miles to Moel-y-fan, Oernant and

The tramroad lift bridge that once carried slate to Pentrefelin mill

Berwyn quarries and was worked by horses. It had a long incline down the mountainside and an impressive stone-built **causeway** ⑩ which can be seen crossing the Eglwyseg valley just north of the canal. The tramway operated until at least 1900.

Another aqueduct was built to cross a river that runs into the Dee. It is very small compared with Chirk and Pontcysyllte, but the **Eglwyseg aqueduct** ⑭ shows the high quality of Telford's masons. The canal is on a causeway with gently curving retaining walls and an arch for the river at the centre. An unusual parapet built from tapering stone blocks put on edge follows the retaining wall for its full length. At the far end of the causeway a **culvert** ⑮ carried the water from Pentre-felin corn mill safely beneath the canal. About 150m further on, **Pentre-felin sluice** ⑯ is an example of one of the features on the canal for controlling water levels. It has been renewed during its lifetime – the wall rebuilt in engineering brick in about 1900 is set between earlier curving stone wing walls.

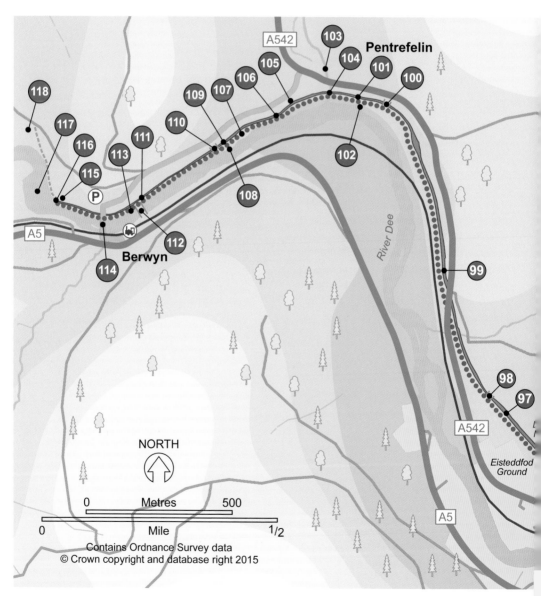

The handsome causeway structure that carried the Oernant tramway from nearby slate quarries to the canal

The curving parapet walls of the Eglwyseg aqueduct

Early nineteenth-century watercolour showing Tŷ Craig stop lock and lift-bridge with horses drawing a wagon up from the smoking limekilns

As you approach Tŷ Craig bridge a bank of four **limekilns** 107 is set into the narrow bank between the canal and river. This was built by the industrialist Exuperius Pickering senior in the early nineteenth century. The limekiln **manager's house** 108 is next to the canal and a private driveway follows a ramp to the bottoms of the kilns for carts to take the burnt quicklime away. A watercolour shows smoke pouring from the kilns and horses struggling up with a wagon. Just before the bridge, **Tŷ Craig stop lock** 109 housed a gate shown in the watercolour that restricted boats from going further up the feeder. The present **Tŷ Craig bridge 48A** 110 must have been built after the watercolour was painted in the early nineteenth century when it was shown as a lift bridge.

The canal is cut from solid rock for its last stretch after Tŷ Craig. It is very narrow but continued to carry traffic as far as **Chain Bridge wharf** 111. The wharf is now beneath part of the Chain Bridge Hotel and its car park. Pickering traded in limestone, bar iron and coal here in the early nineteenth century. Maps and plans show a weighbridge on the wharf for weighing the commodities.

The remarkable **Chain Bridge** 112 across the river Dee was built in 1817 by Pickering to serve his wharf and take goods to the Holyhead Road, where he opened another yard. He had written to the canal committee in 1814 asking permission to build a bridge and a wharf for his exclusive use so that he would have a monopoly of trade on the canal beyond Llangollen. This pioneering suspension bridge may have influenced Thomas Telford two years before he began his great Menai bridge.

Chain Bridge was rebuilt twice – in 1876 and in 1929, after it collapsed in floods. The new bridges were designed by the engineer Sir Henry Robertson and by his son of the same name. The form changed from chains hung below a timber deck in 1817 to the later more conventional suspension bridge, but measured drawings by the French industrial spy J. M. Dutens in 1819 indicate that both rebuildings used the same wrought-iron chains. These may be the oldest suspension bridge chains in Europe still in use. The bridge was closed in 1984 but a restoration scheme by Llantysilio Community Council and Llangollen Town Council has come to its rescue.

The falls of the Dee have long been thought of as a beauty-spot, made even more attractive by the quiet canal feeder. **Chain Bridge Hotel** 113 was built to serve Victorian tourism. Passenger boats brought people from Llangollen, and the suspension bridge linked to Berwyn station on the Llangollen and Corwen Railway, which opened in 1865 and is still used by steam trains. The pedestrian tunnel under the railway has poignant traces of pencil graffiti left by First World War soldiers who were waiting at the station to be taken to the front.

Horse-drawn boats carry passengers from Llangollen

The original Chain Bridge and the Chain Bridge Hotel photographed in about 1870. Pickering's canal wharf was supported by the great retaining wall to the right

The gauge house for controlling the water supply into the canal

The towering **King's Bridge viaduct** ⑭ of 1902–6 carries a road across the river and the canal and creates a remarkable visual grouping of bridges. It threads through one of the arches of the railway viaduct and looms over Chain Bridge.

The last part of the feeder is devoted to managing the water supply. After a mess room for canal maintenance workers and a stop-plank store, a finely built stone building is the **gauge house** ⑮, built in 1947 to control the supply of drinking water to the Cheshire area. A footpath leads on to the **intake gate** from the river and an **overflow sluice** ⑯. A footbridge crosses into the area of parkland around Horseshoe Falls.

The crescent-shaped weir at Horseshoe Falls ⑰ draws water for the whole canal. The elegance of the weir and its setting have made this a popular beauty spot. Jessop proposed the river Dee at Llantysilio as a

water source for the canal in 1795. The weir is placed at a bend in the Dee above rapids. It was designed by Telford and is really J-shaped rather horseshoe-shaped. The crescent form resists the flow of water by spreading the pressure across its length. It also carries floating debris to the ends where it can be removed. The weir is 140m long, with a sloping upstream face but is only 1.22m high, making it less vulnerable to flood damage. It is built of stone with a capping of bull-nosed cast iron which keeps it perfectly level across the width of the river. This ironwork was an innovation when it was added in 1822. Cast iron became widely used for weirs later in the nineteenth century.

Llantysilio church ⑱, a third of a mile north of Horseshoe Falls, is a medieval parish church with a monument to Exuperius Pickering junior in the churchyard.

136

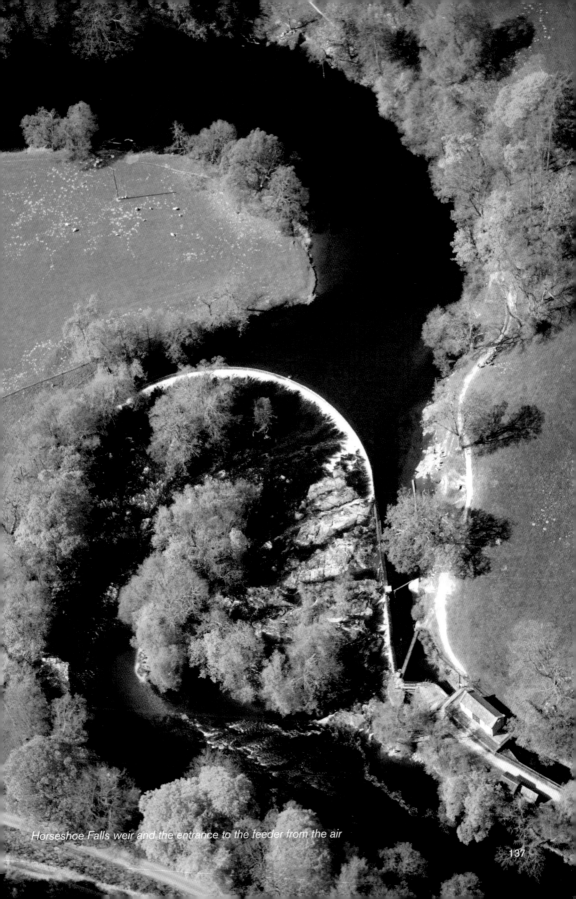

Horseshoe Falls weir and the entrance to the feeder from the air

Llyn Tegid / Lake Bala

Llyn Tegid or Lake Bala is 22 miles west of the nearest part of the canal at Llantysilio. At the time the canal was being built it was already the largest natural lake in Wales, 4 miles long and a mile wide. Jessop saw its potential as a reservoir to ensure a good supply of water down the river Dee to Horseshoe Falls even at times of drought. He recommended a dam to raise the level of the lake by a foot in summer so as to conserve supplies and regulate the flow into the river.

Problems with flooding led to the sluice gates being lowered in 1808 and they were demolished in the 1950s, when the entire river channel below Bala lake was rerouted 100m north. The three-arch stone bridge across the old river course still stands marooned, just south of the present channel.

In the 1830s, Telford devised further systems to conserve water at two lakes high in the Arenig mountains above Bala, Llyn Arenig Fach and Llyn Arenig Fawr. The two lakes fed into the Tryweryn river, which joins the Dee just below Bala lake. As a result of these schemes, the Ellesmere Canal system had one of the most reliable water supplies of any canal. The same supply still feeds the canal and provides drinking water through it to Cheshire.

Llyn Tegid / Lake Bala from the air

Wildlife on the canal

Great care is taken on the canal to ensure that animals, plants and their habitats are safeguarded. The World Heritage site is rich in species and many protected wildlife sites close by are connected by the canal, including the river Dee Special Area of Conservation.

The channel, banks and hedgerows provide homes for many species and make a corridor for animals to move along. Elusive creatures such as otters and water-voles can be seen sometimes in the early morning or late evening, though the signs they leave are easier to find. Water-voles burrow into the banks, eat the grass into close-cropped 'lawns' and leave droppings at the water's edge to mark their territory. Otters, too, mark territory with droppings (known as 'spraint'), which can often be seen under bridges. Wood-mice, newts and toads like dense, dark cover in hedgerows and banks.

Woodlands and grasslands, hedges and verges along the canal may be remnants of the landscape that existed before the canal was built. They provide homes for species that are becoming increasingly rare in the wider countryside, including birds like yellow hammers, song thrushes and tree sparrows. Bridges and tunnels, often built from local stone, provide an important habitat for lichens, mosses and plants. Lichens are very slow growing, and the splodge of colour on a stone wall can take many years to grow. Birds and bats nest or roost in canal structures too. When Pontcysyllte aqueduct was scaffolded for conservation a colony of bats was found in gaps beneath the arches. Even small cracks in bridge and tunnel walls provide shelter for these endangered animals. Pipistrelles, the most common bat in Britain, can fit into a gap the width of a pencil.

The canal at Gledrid

Timeline

1745	William Jessop born
1757	Thomas Telford born
1781	Iron Bridge at Coalbrookdale completed
1789	Discussions by potential investors in building a canal from the Severn to the Mersey
1791	Public meeting held at Ellesmere in Shropshire that agrees to build a canal from the Severn to the Mersey
1792	At the height of the 'Canal Mania', shares in the new Ellesmere Canal Company put on offer and sell out within hours
1793	Jessop appointed as engineer for the Ellesmere Canal; Telford appointed as Agent; Act of Parliament passed for the canal
1795	First section of Ellesmere Canal opens at Chester; construction begins in what is now the World Heritage site
1796	Jessop and Outram build Holmes cast-iron aqueduct on Derby canal; Reynolds and Telford build Longdon-on-Tern cast-iron aqueduct on Shrewsbury Canal
1800	Final decision to keep to the eastern route of the canal and not to build northwards from Pontcysyllte to Chester
1801	Chirk aqueduct is opened, the tallest navigable canal aqueduct in the world before Pontcysyllte. Chirk becomes the terminus of the canal for a short time
1802	Chirk tunnel completed
1804	Work begins on Llangollen branch
1805	Pontcysyllte aqueduct opened 26 November, completing main line of Ellesmere Canal to Trevor
1808	Llangollen branch canal completed
1813	Ellesmere Canal Company and Chester Canal Company merge
1814	William Jessop dies
1834	Thomas Telford dies
1835	Birmingham and Liverpool Junction Canal opens, linking Ellesmere and Chester Canal directly to the Midlands and south of England
1845–6	Ellesmere and Chester Canal takes over Birmingham and Liverpool Junction Canal and forms Shropshire Union Railways and Canal Company
1848	Shrewsbury and Chester Railway completed
1851	Census shows Wales is first country in world with more people working in industry than in agriculture
1857	Shropshire Union Railways and Canal Company leased to London and North Western Railway; Oernant tramway opened from slate quarries to Llangollen branch canal at Pentrefelin
1944	Ellesmere Canal officially abandoned, though it could still be navigated with difficulty
1952	Inland Waterways Association holds rally at Llangollen
1954	British Waterways Board decides to keep the canal open to Llangollen
2009	Pontcysyllte Aqueduct and Canal inscribed by UNESCO onto World Heritage List as site of outstanding universal value
2012	Canal & River Trust created to look after the canals of England and Wales

Further reading

Harry Arnold, *The Llangollen Canal* (Ashbourne, 2008)

Derek Beckett, *Telford's Britain* (London, 1987)

Louis Bergeron, ed., Papers from the Pontcysyllte International Canal Conference: special edition of *Patrimoine de l'industrie/Industrial Patrimony*, volume 17 (2007)

Joseph Boughey and Charles Hadfield, *British Canals: the standard history* (1950, revised edition Stroud, 2008)

Peter Brown, 'The Plas Kynaston Canal', *Journal of the Railway and Canal Historical Society*, 36 (2010)

Anthony Burton, *The Canal Builders* (London, 1972)

Cadw, *Cefn Mawr and District: understanding urban character* (Nantgarw, 2014)

Nigel Crowe, *The English Heritage Book of Canals* (London, 1994)

Charles Hadfield, *The Canals of the West Midlands* (Newton Abbot, 1966)

Charles Hadfield, *The Canal Age* (Newton Abbot, 1968)

Charles Hadfield, *World Canals* (Newton Abbot, 1986)

Charles Hadfield, *Thomas Telford's Temptation* (Cleobury Mortimer, 1993)

Charles Hadfield and A. W. Skempton, *William Jessop: Engineer* (Newton Abbot, 1979)

John Milner and Beryl Williams, *The Rails to Glyn Ceiriog: the history of the Glyn Valley Tramway 1857–1903* (2011)

Rhoda M. Pearce, *Thomas Telford: an illustrated life of Thomas Telford, 1757–1834* (Princes Risborough, 2007)

Jamie Quartermaine, Barrie Trinder and Rick Turner, *Telford's Holyhead Road: the A5 in north Wales* (York, 2003)

L. T. C. Rolt, *Thomas Telford* (London, 1958)

A. W. Skempton, *Civil Engineers and Engineering in Britain, 1600–1830* (Aldershot, 1996)

John Thomas and David Southern, *The Industrial Tramways of the Vale of Llangollen* (Usk, 2013)

Barrie Trinder, *Britain's Industrial Revolution: the making of a manufacturing people, 1700–1870* (Lancaster, 2013)

Peter Wakelin, ed., *Pontcysyllte Aqueduct and Canal Nomination as a World Heritage Site* (Wrexham, 2008)

E. A. Wilson, *The Ellesmere and Llangollen Canal: an historical background* (Chichester, 1975)

Wern Isaf rock cutting

Acknowledgements

The author wishes to thank present and former Royal Commissioners and members of Royal Commission staff for their many contributions to this publication. Rachael Barnwell and Rachel Leung undertook valuable research for the guidebook during Workplace Learning Bursaries with the Commission generously funded by UNESCO Cymru-Wales.

A considerable amount of additional image research was carried out by Jacqueline Humphries of the Canal & River Trust. Staff at the archives, museums and libraries listed in the image credits were extremely helpful. Illustrations were prepared by the Royal Commission, Elizabeth Anne Robinson, Kenning Illustration and the Mapping Company. The photographs amply demonstrate the talent and commitment of Mike Dean (Eye Imagery), Mike Hayward, and the Royal Commission's photographers. I am grateful to the designer Ceri Jones for his care over the layout of the book.

The text was read and commented on by, among others, Peter Brown, Stephen Hughes, Dr Kate Roberts and Andrew Stumpf and by Royal Commissioners Thomas Lloyd, Henry Owen-John, Dr Eurwyn Wiliam and Professor Christopher Williams. Other experts generous in providing advice on this book and the nomination document that preceded it include Peter Birch, Susan Denyer, Dr Dafydd Gwyn, Professor John Hume, Dr Ron Fitzgerald, Stuart Moodie, Dr Sian Rees, Dr Dawn Roberts, Del Roberts-Jones, Dr Barrie Trinder, Rick Turner and Christopher Young.

Chirk